Edexcel
advancing learning, changing lives

Series Editors
Trevor Johnson & Tony Clough

Homework Book

Edexcel
GCSE Mathematics

Foundation Tier
Linear Course

Homework

Chapter 1
Introducing number

Exercise 1A

1

Thousands	Hundreds	Tens	Units

Copy the table of column headings. Use it to write these numbers in figures.

a three hundred and forty six

b four hundred and thirty

c five thousand, two hundred and eighty four

d three thousand and forty nine

e eight thousand and four

2 Copy the table from question 1. Use it to write these numbers in words.

a 36   **b** 456   **c** 208

d 5231   **e** 5093   **f** 6050

3 Copy the table from question 1. Use it to put these numbers in order. Start with the smallest.

a 38   4   12   165

b 456   32   8   4006

c 458   32   1006   755

4 Write the following numbers in order. Start with the smallest.

a fifty four, 304, thirty eight, 450, two hundred and three

b 306, ninety seven, 560, one thousand and twelve

c two thousand and three, 1900, five hundred and twenty four, 736

5 a Write down the value of the 5 in 356

b Write down the value of the 7 in 2791

c Write down the value of the 2 in 2060

6 Write the following numbers in figures.

a eighteen hundred

b twelve thousand, three hundred and twenty four

c twenty two thousand, eight hundred and forty two

d thirteen thousand and forty five

e five hundred thousand

f six million

Exercise 1B

1 Copy the number line and mark the following numbers with an arrow.

a 54   **b** 61   **c** 85   **d** 90   **e** 96

2 Write down the numbers marked on the number line.

3 Copy the number line and mark the following numbers with an arrow.

a 3600   **b** 3850   **c** 3920   **d** 3505   **e** 3965

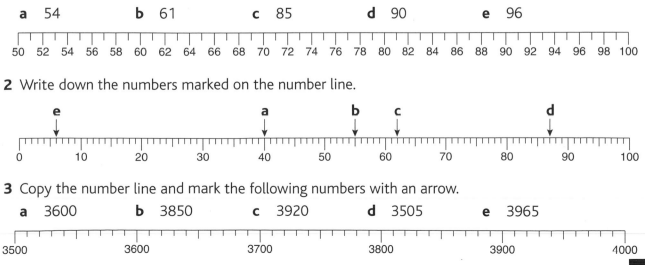

4 Write down the numbers marked on the number line.

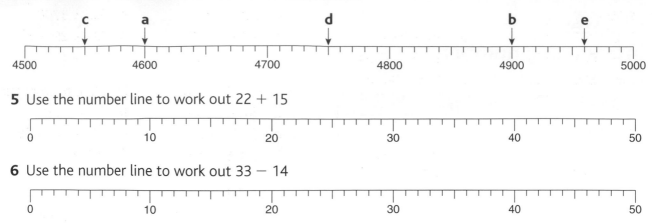

5 Use the number line to work out 22 + 15

```
0        10        20        30        40        50
```

6 Use the number line to work out 33 − 14

```
0        10        20        30        40        50
```

Exercise 1C

1 Write each of the following numbers to the nearest 10

  a 58   **b** 46   **c** 53

  d 89   **e** 7   **f** 97

2 Write each of the following numbers to the nearest 100

  a 358   **b** 825   **c** 407

  d 109   **e** 987   **f** 84

3 Write each of the following numbers to the nearest 1000

  a 3600   **b** 5680   **c** 4267

  d 3059   **e** 4040   **f** 679

4 A salesman drove 1316 miles last month. Write the distance the salesman drove last month correct to the nearest 100 miles.

5 a Write 23 555 correct to the nearest 10 000

  b Write 34 350 correct to the nearest 1000

  c Write 18 399 correct to the nearest 100

  d Ben wins a prize of £28 875. Write this amount correct to the nearest £1000

  e A car costs £23 499. Write this cost correct to the nearest £100

Exercise 1D

1 Work out the following mentally and write down your answer. Jot down any numbers you wish.

  a 15 + 25   **b** 18 + 33   **c** 53 + 61

  d 56 + 65   **e** 51 + 19   **f** 28 − 15

  g 40 − 16   **h** 54 − 16   **i** 43 − 27

2 Work out the following and write down your answer. Show any working.

  a Add the answer to 3 × 5 to the answer to 4 × 6

  b What is the difference between the answer to 7 × 6 and the answer to 3 × 8?

3 Copy and complete this multiplication table.

×	4		6
		50	60
7			
	20		

4 a Find the cost of two tins of paint at £2.99 each.

  b Find the cost of 3 bottles of drink at 99p each.

  c Find the cost of 6 rolls of wallpaper at £7.99 a roll.

  d A battery costs 95p. Find the cost of 5 batteries.

  e A computer costs £499. Find the cost of 5 computers.

Exercise 1E

1 Work out

a 227 + 138   b 48 + 256

c 607 + 178   d 3865 + 2304

e 3909 + 2604   f 474 + 3046

g 28 + 5984

2 Work out

a 786 − 126   b 438 − 136

c 985 − 561   d 500 − 167

e 406 − 138

3 Find the missing numbers

a 347 + ? = 450   b ? + 286 = 500

c 326 − ? = 201   d ? − 332 = 218

4 The sum of two numbers is 677. One of the numbers is 296. Find the other number.

5 The sum of three numbers is 1000
Two of the numbers are 314 and 298
Find the third number.

6 The difference between two numbers is 164
The larger of the two numbers is 308
Work out the smaller number.

7 The difference between two numbers is 306
The smaller of the two numbers is 266
Find the larger number.

Exercise 1F

1 24 × 3   **2** 25 × 4   **3** 21 × 5

4 22 × 4   **5** 33 × 5   **6** 27 × 6

7 46 × 7   **8** 82 × 6   **9** 54 × 7

10 422 × 6   **11** 426 × 6   **12** 734 × 6

13 157 × 8   **14** 417 × 7   **15** 543 × 9

Exercise 1G

1 10 × 8   **2** 10 × 18   **3** 10 × 28

4 20 × 80   **5** 30 × 21   **6** 21 × 34

7 36 × 23   **8** 24 × 35   **9** 42 × 36

10 46 × 33   **11** 61 × 32   **12** 54 × 62

13 27 × 84

14 Use the fact that 29 × 37 = 1073 to work out

a 290 × 37   b 29 × 3700

c 290 × 370   d 10 × 29 × 37

e 1073 ÷ 29

15 Use the fact that 57 × 88 = 5016 to work out

a 57 × 8800   b 570 × 88

c 570 × 880   d 57 × 10 × 88

e 5016 ÷ 88   f 50 160 ÷ 57

Exercise 1H

1 36 ÷ 3   **2** 48 ÷ 5   **3** 66 ÷ 5

4 75 ÷ 5   **5** 76 ÷ 3   **6** 234 ÷ 3

7 128 ÷ 4   **8** 324 ÷ 6   **9** 573 ÷ 6

10 432 ÷ 6   **11** 404 ÷ 5   **12** 567 ÷ 9

13 257 ÷ 9   **14** 633 ÷ 9   **15** 754 ÷ 8

Exercise 1I

1 288 ÷ 15   **2** 490 ÷ 25

3 577 ÷ 17   **4** 432 ÷ 24

5 477 ÷ 23   **6** 674 ÷ 42

7 985 ÷ 21   **8** 1211 ÷ 22

9 1407 ÷ 37   **10** 1888 ÷ 45

Exercise 1J

1 A calculator costs £7.35. Find the cost of 14 calculators.

2 Cans of drink are packed into boxes holding 36 cans. How many boxes can be completely filled from 840 cans?

3 Kerry gets paid £7.45 for each hour that she works. How much does she get paid for 27 hours work?

4 A machine fills 425 bottles with lemonade each hour. How many hours will it take the machine to fill 9775 bottles with lemonade?

5 There were 12 560 adults and 4570 children at a rugby game. Each adult paid £15.50 and each child paid £8.50. Work out the total amount paid.

6 Emma works for 38 hours in a week. She gets paid £247. Work out how much she gets paid for an hour's work.

7 A shop sells 26 super size televisions at £495 each and 34 standard size televisions at £279 each. Work out the total cost of the televisions sold.

8 Matt gets paid £6.80 for each hour he works during weekdays. He gets paid £10.20 for each hour he works at the weekend. In one week, he works 38 hours on weekdays and 8 hours at the weekend. Work out the total amount he should get paid.

Exercise 1K

1 There were 108 people on a train before it got to a station. At the station 38 people got off and 25 got on the train. How many people are there now on the train?

2 a Work out how many 28p stamps can be bought for £2.
  b Work out the change.

3 It costs 20p to park for 10 minutes in Bristol. How much would it cost to park for 1 hour?

4 A can of drink costs 75p. Work out the cost of 5 cans of drink.

5 A coffee costs 84p and a cake costs 99p. Work out the cost of 2 coffees and 3 cakes.

6 A train travels 256 km every day it is in service. Work out how far it travels during 50 days in service.

7 7 people share a prize of £651. Work out how much they each get.

8 A packet of biscuits contains 12 biscuits. How many biscuits are there in 24 packets?

9 A crate holds 15 bottles. How many crates are needed to hold 345 bottles?

10 A car dealer has to pay £5845 for each new car he orders. He orders 11 new cars. Work out how much he has to pay.

Exercise 1L

1 Check these calculations by rounding and writing a rough answer.
  a $47 \times 61 = 247$
  b $32 \times 51 = 152$
  c $103 \times 29 = 2987$
  d $199 \times 99 = 19\,701$
  e $204 \times 302 = 6168$

2 Check these calculations by using the inverse operation.
  a $603 - 158 = 445$
  b $425 - 329 = 106$
  c $812 - 659 = 247$
  d $3584 - 2312 = 1272$
  e $3206 - 159 = 3153$

3 The distance from home to work is 42 km. Ben makes the journey to work and back 38 times. Ben calculates that the total distance travelled is 3192 km. Use rounding to check whether he is correct.

4 Check these calculations using the inverse operation. Use a calculator.
  a $48 \times 54 = 2592$
  b $408 \times 206 = 84\,048$
  c $864 \div 36 = 24$
  d $8064 \div 96 = 48$
  e $40\,096 \div 128 = 32$

Exercise 1M

1 List all of the factors of the following numbers.
  a 9 **b** 6 **c** 12 **d** 14 **e** 18
  f 30 **g** 22 **h** 27 **i** 48 **j** 80

2 List all the common factors of the following pairs of numbers.
  a 4 and 6   **b** 3 and 6
  c 8 and 10   **d** 10 and 12
  e 10 and 15   **f** 7 and 14
  g 14 and 21   **h** 30 and 45
  i 16 and 24

3 Write down the first three multiples of the following numbers.

    a 4   **b** 6   **c** 2   **d** 9   **e** 20

4 Write down

    a the third square number

    b the cube of 10

    c the sum of the fourth square number and the fifth square number

    d the product of the second square number and the third square number

    e the fifth cube number minus 1

Exercise 1N

1 Work out

    a $4 \times 5 - 6$ **b** $6 \times 4 - 8$

    c $5 \times 5 + 6$ **d** $4 + 5 \times 6$

    e $3 + 5 \times 4$ **f** $24 - 5 \times 4$

    g $9 \times 5 - 16$ **h** $44 - 5 \times 6$

    i $34 + 8 \times 5$ **j** $49 - 7 \times 7$

2 Work out

    a $15 - 6 - 7$ **b** $25 - 16 - 4$

    c $22 - 6 + 7$ **d** $30 - 16 + 9$

    e $18 + 6 - 8$ **f** $30 + 16 - 17$

    g $45 - 45 + 17$

3 Work out

    a $10 \div 2 + 3$ **b** $16 \div 4 + 4$

    c $30 + 10 \div 5$ **d** $24 - 12 \div 3$

    e $40 - 20 \div 2$

4 Work out

    a $3 \times (2 + 4)$ **b** $4 \times (8 - 4)$

    c $(12 + 4) \times 2$ **d** $13 - (5 + 4)$

    e $18 - (15 - 4)$ **f** $20 + (5 - 4)$

    g $(8 + 4) \div 2$ **h** $(17 + 4) \div 3$

    i $20 \div (5 - 3)$ **j** $18 \div (7 - 4)$

5 Add brackets so that each answer is correct.

    a $20 - 5 - 4 = 19$ **b** $18 - 6 \div 4 = 3$

    c $2 + 5 \times 4 = 28$ **d** $12 - 5 + 4 = 3$

    e $30 \div 5 - 4 = 30$ **f** $32 \div 4 - 2 = 6$

    g $40 - 5 \div 5 = 7$ **h** $40 - 5 \div 5 = 39$

    i $10 + 5 \times 5 = 35$ **j** $10 + 5 \times 5 = 75$

6 Use a calculator to work out the following

    a $(36 + 48) \times 27$ **b** $(146 + 57) \times 38$

    c $86 + 48 \times 35$ **d** $2036 + 45 \times 17$

    e $864 - 16 \times 18$ **f** $3456 \div 18 - 192$

    g $(536 - 48) \times 52$

7 Use a calculator to work out the following

    a $(236 + 418) \times (127 - 86)$

    b $(98 - 9) \times (197 - 86)$

    c $24 \times 36 - (627 - 96)$

    d $\dfrac{44 \times 86}{88}$ **e** $\dfrac{18\,816}{28 \times 42}$

    f $\dfrac{45 \times 56}{191 - 101}$ **g** $\dfrac{236 + 1078}{247 - 174}$

    h $\dfrac{529}{23} + \dfrac{1152}{24}$

Exercise 1O

1 Find the three prime numbers between 40 and 50

2 Write the following numbers as products of their prime factors.

    a 12   **b** 16   **c** 18   **d** 24

    e 28   **f** 40   **g** 54   **h** 44

    i 84   **j** 100

3 Find the highest common factor (HCF) of the following pairs of numbers.

    a 14 and 16   **b** 15 and 20

    c 20 and 30   **d** 54 and 72

    e 72 and 96

4 Find the lowest common multiple (LCM) of the following pairs of numbers

    a 3 and 4   **b** 5 and 10

    c 8 and 12   **d** 24 and 36

    e 25 and 30

5 a Find the number of multiples of 7 that are less than 100

    b Find the number of multiples of 9 that are less than 100

6 Which of the following numbers are factors of 1440?

2   3   5   7   11   15   20   25   30

7 Write each of the numbers as a product of its prime factors.

a   210   b   315

c   2002   d   316

e   1296   f   1575

8 Find the lowest common multiple of the following pairs of numbers.

a   28 and 49   b   36 and 96

c   23 and 29   d   75 and 125

e   128 and 192

Chapter 2
Collecting and recording data

Exercise 2A

1 Mason carried out a survey on the colour of each of the first 20 cars passing his house. Here are his results.

red	white	silver	blue	silver
black	white	red	silver	blue
red	silver	green	silver	black
red	white	silver	red	white

a   Copy and complete the data collection sheet to show this information.

Colour	Tally	Frequency

b   Write down the name of the most popular colour.

2 Here is a data collection sheet. It shows information about the numbers of children in some families.

Number of children	Tally	Frequency
0	卌 ||	
1	卌 |	
2	卌 ||||	
3	||||	
4	|||	

a   Complete the frequency column.

b   Write down the number of families with 2 children.

c   Find the total number of families.

3 Jenny asks each of her friends to name their favourite type of music.
Draw a suitable data collection sheet that Jenny could use to record this information.

4 Jamilla spins a spinner 50 times.
Here are the scores on the spinner for each of the 50 spins.

1	3	2	3	4	2	3	3	2	3
2	1	3	4	2	3	2	2	1	2
3	4	2	3	3	3	2	1	4	2
2	2	2	1	2	3	1	3	4	3
4	1	2	3	3	2	2	2	3	4

a   Draw a tally chart to show this information.

b   Is the spinner fair or biased? Explain your answer.

5 Mr. Johnson asks some students to name their favourite subject at school. He records their answers in this data collection sheet.

Subject	Tally	Frequency
English	||||	
Maths	卌	
Science	|||	
P.E.	卌 卌 ||	

He then asks another six students.
Here are their answers,

	English	English	Maths
	P.E.	Science	P.E.

a Complete the frequency table.

b Write down the most popular subject.

c Work out the total number of students Mr Johnson asks.

Exercise 2B

1 Cliff carries out a survey of students in his class.
The data collected includes

colour of hair   height   weight
key stage 3 Maths level   IQ

Which data collected is

a discrete

b continuous ?

2 A student wanted to find out how many pizzas adults eat. He used this question in a questionnaire.

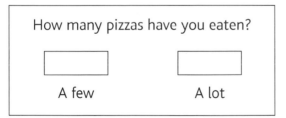

How many pizzas have you eaten?

A few	A lot

a Write down **two** things that are wrong with this question.

b Design a better question that the student can use to find out how many pizzas adults eat.
You should include some response boxes.
(1387 June 2006)

3 Write down two things which are wrong with each of the following questions.

a "How much television do you watch?"

not much   average   lots

b "How much pocket money do you get each week?"

£1–£2   £2–£3   £3–£4   £4–£5

4 Michelle wants to find out how often people visit the local library .

a Design a suitable question to find out how often people visit the local library.

Michelle decides to use a sample of 100 people. She stands by the entrance to the library on a Monday morning and gives a questionnaire to each of the first 100 people that she meets.

b i What is wrong with this sample?
ii How could Michelle get a better sample?

5 Write down five questions that might appear in a questionnaire on the types of restaurants people prefer. Describe how this information might be collected and recorded.

Exercise 2C

1 The database contains some information about the people living in a street

House number	Number of occupants	Number of pets	Number of cars
1	3	2	2
2	6	0	3
3	2	4	1
4	3	2	3
5	4	1	2

Using this database,

a write down the number of pets at house number 3

b write down the number of occupants at house number 2

c write down the number of houses with more than 1 car.

d write down the total number of pets in the five houses.

2 This database contains information about some students.

Using the database,

a write down Zach's age.

b write down Melissa's IQ.

c write down the name of the oldest female.

d who has an IQ under 100?

e who has the highest IQ?

f how many students are under 14 years of age?

g list the girls in order of IQ, highest IQ first.

Name	Gender	Age	IQ
Jessica	female	12	101
Daniel	male	11	112
Mason	male	13	102
Samantha	female	16	98
Melissa	female	13	105
Zach	male	13	97
Georgina	female	15	95
Marc	male	16	100
Alfie	male	12	104
Helen	female	13	120

3 The database contains some information about the cost (in £) of holidays at a Spanish hotel.

Month	4 nights	7 nights	10 nights	14 nights
April	385	495	619	775
May	499	615	755	919
June	465	605	755	935
July	535	705	895	1105
August	605	775	945	1169
September	535	675	829	999
October	525	685	799	949

Using this database,

a write down the cost of a holiday for 14 nights in June.

b write down the cost of a holiday for 4 nights in May.

c write down the holidays which cost over £1000

d write down a list of all of the holidays which cost less than £500

4 Joanna wants to find out if females with blue eyes watch more television than other females.

Name	Age	Month of birth	Gender	Colour of eyes	Favourite colour	Favourite sport	Favourite Capital City	TV hours watched per week	Number of pets
Angela	29	April	Female	Blue	Red	Football	Amsterdam	25	1
Bryony	16	June	Female	Green	Black	Tennis	London	34	4
Caroline	35	December	Female	Blue	Green	Pool	Madrid	18	7
David	13	May	Male	Brown	Blue	Baseball	Paris	22	3
Elaine	21	September	Female	Green	White	Rugby	London	42	0

Joanna does not need to use all of this database.
Which parts of the database should she use?

Chapter 3
Angles 1

Exercise 3A

1 Copy and complete each of these statements.

  a There are ....° in a full turn.

  b There are ....° in a half turn.

  c There are ....° in a quarter turn.

  d There are ....° in a right angle.

2 For each clock, write down the size of the angle shown between the hands.

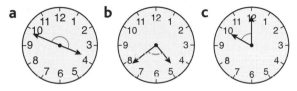

3 Find the size of the angle between the hands of a clock at 11 o'clock.

4 a

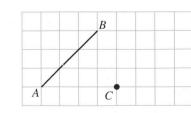

  i Name angle x in two different ways.

  ii Give the special name of this type of angle.

  b Name the right angle in two different ways.

  c Name the horizontal side of the triangle.

  d Name the vertical side of the triangle.

5

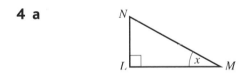

Copy the diagram and draw a line through C which is

a parallel to the line AB

b perpendicular to the line AB.

6 What type of angle is

  a angle w

  b angle x

  c angle y.

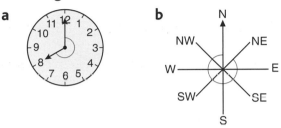

7 Work out the size of the angle the *hour* hand of a clock turns in

  a 3 hours   **b** 1 hour

  c 5 hours   **d** 8 hours.

8 Find the size of the reflex angle shown in each diagram.

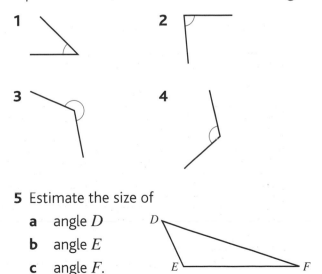

9 Work out the size of the *reflex* angle between

  a the hands of a clock at 1 o'clock

  b South and North East.

10 Work out the size of the angle the *minute* hand of a clock turns in

  a 45 minutes   **b** 35 minutes

  c 50 minutes.

Exercise 3B

In questions **1–4**, estimate the size of the angle.

1   **2**

3   **4**

5 Estimate the size of

  a angle D

  b angle E

  c angle F.

Exercise 3C

In Questions **1–3**, estimate the size of the angles and then measure them with a protractor.

1

2

3

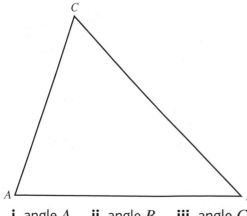

4 a For each of these angles, estimate its size and then measure it with a protractor.

i angle A **ii** angle B **iii** angle C.

b Measure the length of each of these lines.
i AB **ii** BC **iii** AC.

Exercise 3D

In Questions **1–15**, use a protractor to draw the angles.

1 30°   **2** 160°   **3** 250°   **4** 340°

5 75°   **6** 325°   **7** 145°   **8** 265°

9 47°   **10** 119°   **11** 94°   **12** 139°

13 283°   **14** 19°   **15** 352°

16 a Draw a line LM.
b Angle $MLN = 41°$. Draw angle MLN.

17 a Draw a line XY.
b Angle $XYZ = 163°$. Draw angle XYZ.

In Questions **18–21**, sketches of triangles are shown. Make an accurate drawing of each of these triangles.

18   **19**

20   **21**

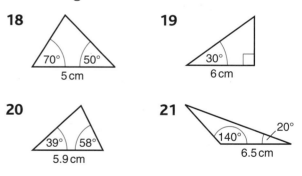

22 a Draw a line PQ 6.7 cm long.
b With PQ as base, draw triangle PQR where angle $PQR = 56°$ and angle $QPR = 37°$.
c Measure the length of PR.

23 a Draw a line TU 5.9 cm long.
b With TU as base, draw triangle TUV where angle $TUV = 139°$ and angle $UTV = 21°$.
c Measure the length of UV.

24 a Draw triangle ABC with $AB = 6.4$ cm, angle $ABC = 96°$ and angle $BAC = 32°$.
b Measure the size of angle ACB.

25 Here is a sketch of a quadrilateral *PQRS*. *PR* is a *diagonal* of the quadrilateral.
PR = 5.2 cm.
Angle *SPR* = 41°,
angle *SRP* = 36°,
angle *RPQ* = 58° and
angle *PRQ* = 48°.
Make an accurate drawing of *PQRS*.

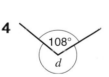

26 a Draw a line *AB* 6 cm long.
  b Try to construct a triangle *ABC* with angle *ABC* = 120° and angle *BAC* = 60°. What happens?

Exercise 3E

The diagrams in this exercise are not accurately drawn.

In Questions **1–7**, find the size of each angle marked with a letter.

1
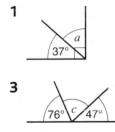

2

3
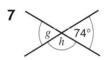

4

5

6

7

8 In the diagram, *ABC* is a straight line.

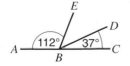

  a Work out the size of angle *DBE*.
  b Give a reason for your answer.

9 In the diagram, three lines cross at a point.

  a Find the value of **i** *x* **ii** *y*
  b Give a reason for each answer.

10 The diagram is wrong. Explain why.

11 In the diagram, *PQ* and *RS* are straight lines which cross at *T*. *TU* is a straight line.

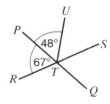

Find the sizes of these angles and give a reason for each answer.

  a angle *QTS*
  b angle *STU*
  c angle *RTQ*.

In Questions **12–16**, find the size of each of the angles marked with a letter.

12

13

14

15

16

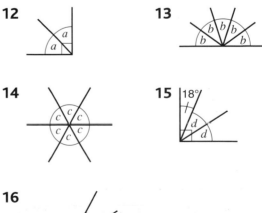

Chapter 4
Fractions and decimals

Exercise 4A

In questions **1** to **3** write down the fraction of the shape that is **i** shaded **ii** unshaded

1 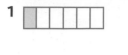 **2** 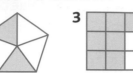 **3**

4 There are 28 students in a class.
5 of the students wear glasses.
What fraction of the class

 a wear glasses

 b do not wear glasses?

5 There are 3 green and 5 red apples in a bowl.
What fraction of the apples are

 a green **b** red?

6 Kevin holds 2 red, 3 blue and 4 green cards.
What fraction of Kevin's cards are

 a red **b** green?

7 Susie gets £5 pocket money. She saves £2 of her pocket money. What fraction of her pocket money does Susie save?

8 There are 30 questions in a test. Jamilla gets 17 of the questions correct.
What fraction of the questions in the test does Jamilla get **wrong**?

Exercise 4B

In questions **1** to **10**, copy the fractions and fill in the missing number to make the fractions equivalent.

1 $\frac{1}{2} = \frac{}{10}$ **2** $\frac{1}{6} = \frac{}{12}$ **3** $\frac{2}{3} = \frac{}{12}$

4 $\frac{5}{6} = \frac{}{12}$ **5** $\frac{2}{5} = \frac{}{15}$ **6** $\frac{3}{7} = \frac{9}{}$

7 $\frac{4}{5} = \frac{}{25}$ **8** $\frac{9}{10} = \frac{36}{}$ **9** $\frac{8}{11} = \frac{}{55}$

10 $\frac{7}{20} = \frac{}{80}$

In questions **11** to **16** copy the diagram and shade the given fraction

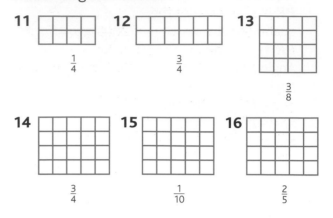

11 $\frac{1}{4}$ **12** $\frac{3}{4}$ **13** $\frac{3}{8}$

14 $\frac{3}{4}$ **15** $\frac{1}{10}$ **16** $\frac{2}{5}$

Exercise 4C

In questions **1** to **10** write each fraction in its simplest form.

1 $\frac{4}{8}$ **2** $\frac{3}{12}$ **3** $\frac{12}{15}$ **4** $\frac{10}{30}$

5 $\frac{8}{10}$ **6** $\frac{30}{40}$ **7** $\frac{15}{35}$ **8** $\frac{48}{60}$

9 $\frac{75}{100}$ **10** $\frac{90}{150}$

In questions **11** to **14** write down the fraction of the shape that is shaded. Give each fraction in its simplest form.

11 **12**

13 **14**

In questions **15** and **16** give each fraction in its simplest form.

15 Tom has 12 t-shirts. 4 of the t-shirts are red.
Write down the fraction of the t-shirts that are red.

16 There are 32 cars in a car park.
18 of the cars are blue.
Write down the fraction of the cars that are **not** blue.

17 The Maldives is a country made up of 2000 islands.
People live on only 220 of these islands.
Write 220 as a fraction of 2000
Give your fraction in its simplest form.
(1388 January 2005)

18 There are 30 students in a class.
20 of these students are female.
Find the fraction of the class that is female.
Give your fraction in its simplest form.
(1388 March 2004)

19 Anil sold his car for £600
He put £250 of the £600 in a bank account.
Write £250 as a fraction of £600
Give your answer as a fraction in its simplest form. *(1388 March 2003)*

Exercise 4D

In questions **1** to **8** write the fractions in order of size. Start with the smallest fraction.

1 $\frac{1}{4}$ $\frac{3}{8}$

2 $\frac{5}{6}$ $\frac{2}{3}$

3 $\frac{11}{30}$ $\frac{2}{5}$ $\frac{4}{15}$

4 $\frac{1}{4}$ $\frac{3}{20}$ $\frac{2}{5}$

5 $\frac{5}{8}$ $\frac{3}{4}$ $\frac{7}{16}$

6 $\frac{9}{32}$ $\frac{3}{4}$ $\frac{7}{16}$ $\frac{5}{8}$

7 $\frac{11}{40}$ $\frac{1}{2}$ $\frac{9}{20}$ $\frac{3}{5}$

8 $\frac{3}{4}$ $\frac{5}{6}$ $\frac{7}{12}$ $\frac{13}{24}$

9 Sally says that $\frac{7}{10}$ is smaller than $\frac{9}{20}$ because 7 is smaller than 9. Is Sally correct? Give a reason for your answer.

10 Ed and Jo have identical cans of cola. Ed drinks $\frac{4}{5}$ of his cola. Jo drinks $\frac{7}{9}$ of her cola. Who has drunk the most? Give a reason for your answer.

Exercise 4E

In questions **1** and **2** write down the length of each pencil.

1

2

In questions **3** and **4** write down the weight of the parcel.

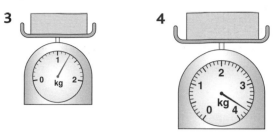

5 Write down the number that each arrow is pointing to on the scales.

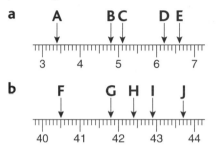

In questions **6** and **7** write down the weight shown on each scale.

6 **7**

Exercise 4F

1 Write down the value of the 7 in each number.

	thousands	hundreds	tens	units		tenths	hundredths	thousandths
a			7	8	.	1	3	
b		4	1	7	.	9		
c				0	.	5	7	1
d	7	3	4	5	.	3		
e				6	.	7	2	5

2 Write down the value of the 2 in each number.

   a 62.45   **b** 248.9   **c** 8.321

   d 0.276   **e** 4.672

3 Write down the value of the 8 in each number.

  a 5.48   **b** 378.1   **c** 9.08

  d 876.9   **e** 6.824

4 Write down the number that each arrow is pointing to on the scales.

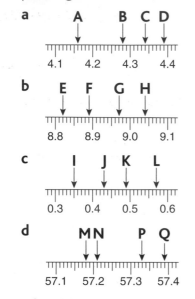

a A   B C D

    4.1   4.2   4.3   4.4

b E F   G H

    8.8   8.9   9.0   9.1

c I   J K   L

    0.3   0.4   0.5   0.6

d M N   P Q

    57.1 57.2 57.3 57.4

Exercise 4G

In questions **1** to **10** write the numbers in order of size. Start with the smallest number each time.

1

tens	units		tenths	hundredths	thousandths
3	4	.	5	6	2
3	4	.	5	5	
3	4	.	5	6	8

2

units		tenths	hundredths	thousandths
8	.	2	1	3
8	.	2	2	
8	.	2	2	1

3 9.42, 9.24, 9.44

4 6.37, 6.77, 6.73, 6.7

5 0.85, 0.58, 0.5, 0.8

6 59.12, 59.21, 59.2, 59.11

7 7.263, 7.236, 7.632, 7.623, 7.362

8 0.183, 0.831, 0.138, 0.18, 0.31

9 4.062, 4.026, 4.002, 4.06, 4.022

10 9.317, 9.71, 9.713, 9.137, 9.13

11 The table shows the heights, in metres, of five students. Write down the students in order of height. Start with the tallest student.

Emily	1.55 m
Prateek	1.78 m
Tasha	1.7 m
Josie	1.5 m
Jonathan	1.69 m

12 The table shows the time, in seconds, in which five swimmers swam 50 m. Write down the order in which the swimmers finished the race.

Sharon	28.13 s
Helen	28.31 s
Farah	28.3 s
Neela	28.33 s
Paula	28.1 s

Exercise 4H

1 Write the decimals as fractions

	units		tenths	hundredths	thousandths
a	0	.	9		
b	0	.	0	3	
c	0	.	3	7	
d	0	.	8	1	9
e	0	.	0	0	3

In questions **2** to **15** write each of the decimals as a fraction in its simplest form.

2 0.4   **3** 0.32   **4** 0.239

5 0.06   **6** 0.008   **7** 0.017

8 0.48   **9** 0.6   **10** 0.125

11 3.4   **12** 9.01   **13** 43.2

14 8.43   **15** 10.003

Exercise 4I

1 Write the following fractions as decimals

    a $\frac{3}{10}$ **b** $\frac{13}{100}$ **c** $\frac{9}{100}$ **d** $\frac{129}{1000}$ **e** $\frac{7}{1000}$

2 Write the following as equivalent fractions and then as decimals

    a $\frac{3}{5} = \frac{}{10}$ **b** $\frac{9}{20} = \frac{}{100}$ **c** $\frac{21}{50} = \frac{}{100}$

    d $\frac{13}{500} = \frac{}{1000}$ **e** $\frac{8}{25} = \frac{}{100}$

3 Write down the following fractions as decimals

    a $\frac{1}{10}$ **b** $\frac{1}{100}$ **c** $\frac{1}{2}$ **d** $\frac{1}{4}$ **e** $\frac{3}{4}$

4 Use short division to change these fractions to decimals

    a $\frac{4}{5}$ **b** $\frac{1}{8}$

5 Use a calculator to change these fractions to decimals

    a $\frac{1}{16}$ **b** $\frac{17}{40}$ **c** $\frac{123}{160}$ **d** $\frac{19}{25}$ **e** $\frac{21}{32}$

6 Use a calculator to change these fractions to decimals

    a $\frac{5}{6}$ **b** $\frac{8}{11}$ **c** $\frac{7}{15}$ **d** $\frac{23}{24}$ **e** $\frac{3}{7}$

Chapter 5
Two-dimensional shapes

Exercise 5A

1 Here are 8 letters.

    A   F   H   N   P   S   U   X

    a Write down the two letters which have exactly **one** line of symmetry.

    b Write down the two letters which have rotational symmetry of order 2 and **two** lines of symmetry.

    c Write down the two letters which have rotational symmetry of order 2 and **no** lines of symmetry.

(4400 May 2005)

2 Here is a list of 8 numbers.

    11   16   18   36   68   69   82   88

From these numbers, write down a number which has
    i exactly **one** line of symmetry,
    ii 2 lines of symmetry **and** rotational symmetry of order 2
    iii rotational symmetry of order 2 but **no** lines of symmetry.

(1387 June 2005)

3 Copy and draw in all the lines of symmetry on each of the following flags.

(1384 June 1997)

4 On the grid, 10 squares are shaded. Copy the diagram and shade **one** extra square so that the shaded shape has **one** line of symmetry.

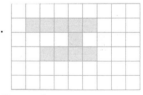

(1388 June 2003)

5 The diagram shows part of a shape. The shape has rotational symmetry of order 4 about the point P.

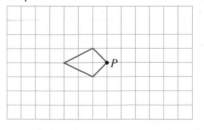

On a copy of the diagram, complete the shape.

(1387 November 2004)

6 a On the grid, 6 squares are shaded.
Copy the diagram and shade one more square so that the shaded shape has one line of symmetry.

b On the grid, 4 squares are shaded.
Copy the diagram and shade one more square so that the shaded shape has rotational symmetry of order 2 *(1388 April 2006)*

7 A pattern is to be drawn. It will have rotational symmetry of order 4

The pattern has been started. By shading **six** more squares, complete the pattern. *(1388 January 2003)*

Exercise 5B

1 Here are 7 quadrilaterals.

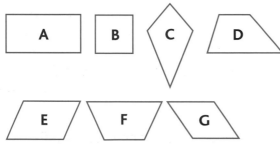

Give the special name of each of the quadrilaterals.

2 a A triangle is shown on a grid of centimetre squares.

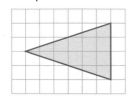

　i Write down the special name of this type of triangle.
　ii On a copy of this diagram, draw the line of symmetry of the triangle.

　iii Measure and write down the size of the smallest angle of the triangle.

b **i** Draw a quadrilateral that has exactly one line of symmetry.
　ii Write down the special name of your quadrilateral.

3 Here are 7 triangles.

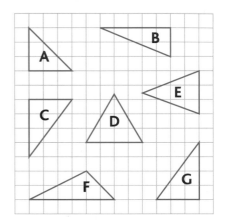

a Write down the letter of the triangle that is
　i equilateral
　ii both isosceles **and** right-angled.
　　　　　　　　　(1388 April 2006)

b Write down the letter of a triangle that is
　i isosceles **but not** right-angled
　ii right angled **but not** isosceles.

4 Here are four quadrilaterals labelled **A**, **B**, **C** and **D**.

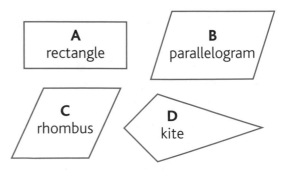

a Write down the letter of the quadrilateral which has
　i exactly one line of symmetry
　ii **no** lines of symmetry
　iii **both** diagonals as lines of symmetry.

b Write down the letter of the quadrilateral which **does not** have rotational symmetry of order 2

(1388 January 2005)

Exercise 5C

1 Explain why a rectangle is not a regular polygon.

2 Explain why this shape is not a polygon.

3 a Draw a sketch of a regular polygon with rotational symmetry of order 5

b Give the mathematical name of your polygon.

c On your sketch, draw the lines of symmetry of the polygon.

4 Here is a regular polygon.

a Give the mathematical name of this polygon.

b Describe fully the symmetry properties of this polygon.

5 The 6-sided polygon is made from a square and 2 equilateral triangles.

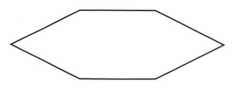

a Write down the special name for a 6-sided polygon.

b Explain why this polygon is not a regular polygon.

c For the polygon, write down
  i how many lines of symmetry it has
  ii its order of rotational symmetry.
  (4400 November 2005)

Exercise 5D

1 Use ruler and compasses to **construct** this triangle accurately.

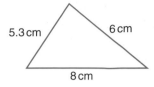

You must show all construction lines. Measure and write down the size of the smallest angle in the triangle.

2 Use ruler and compasses to **construct** this triangle accurately.

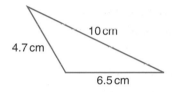

You must show all construction lines. Measure and write down the size of the largest angle in the triangle.

3 Use ruler and compasses to **construct** an equilateral triangle with sides of length 6 centimetres.

You must show all construction lines.
(1387 June 2005)

4 The diagram shows the triangle ABD.

a Make an accurate drawing of the triangle ABD.

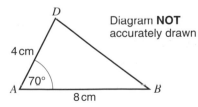

Diagram **NOT** accurately drawn

b C is the point so that $ABCD$ is a parallelogram.
Mark the position of C with a cross (**X**).
Label the point C.

5 ABCD is a rhombus of side 7 cm.
The length of the diagonal BD is 6 cm.

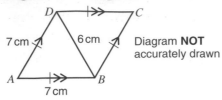

Diagram **NOT** accurately drawn

Use ruler and compasses to **construct** the rhombus ABCD.
You must show **all** construction lines.

(5540 June 2005)

6 ABCD is a quadrilateral.
AB = 6 cm. AC = 9 cm. BC = 5 cm.
Angle BAD = 66°. AD = 3.5 cm.
Make an accurate drawing of the quadrilateral ABCD. *(1385 November 2001)*

7 The diagram shows a sketch of a triangle.

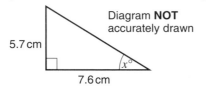

Diagram **NOT** accurately drawn

5.7 cm

7.6 cm

a Make an accurate drawing of the triangle.
b i Using your drawing, measure and write down the size of the angle marked $x°$.
 ii Write down the special mathematical name of the angle marked $x°$.

(1385 November 2000)

Exercise 5E

1 Here are 7 triangles.

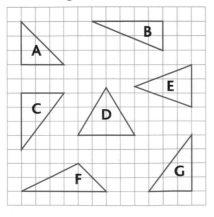

Write down the letters of the pair of congruent triangles. *(1388 April 2006)*

2 Here are 8 quadrilaterals.

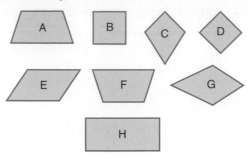

Write down **two** pairs of quadrilaterals which are congruent.

3 Here are nine shapes.

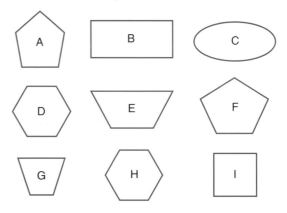

i Write down the letter of a shape that is a pentagon.
ii Write down the letters of the pair of congruent shapes.

(1388 April 2005)

4 Two of the triangles are congruent.

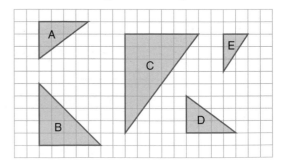

a Write down the letters of these two triangles.

One of the triangles is isosceles.

b Write down the letter of the isosceles triangle.

(1388 January 2004)

Exercise 5F

1 a Copy this diagram and label these lines with their names.

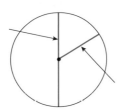

b Copy this diagram and label the two lines with their names and the part of the circle with its name.

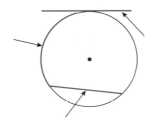

c Copy this diagram and label the parts of the circle with their names.

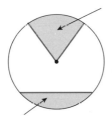

2 Draw accurately a circle of radius 4 cm.

(1388 November 2005)

3 The diagram shows a straight line PQ.

a Measure the length, in cm, of the line PQ.

P ————————————— Q

PQ is a radius of a circle. The point P is the centre of the circle.

b On a copy of the diagram, draw the circle, centre P, radius PQ.

c Write down the length, in cm, of the diameter of this circle.

d On your diagram, mark with a cross (**✗**), a point on the circumference of the circle. Label this point R.

4 A ————————————— B

a Measure the length of the line AB. Give your answer in millimetres.

b Draw a circle which would have AB as a diameter.

Exercise 5G

1 On a copy of this diagram, show how the shaded shape will tessellate.

You should draw at least another eight shapes.

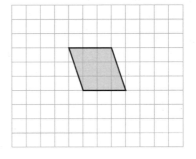

2 On a copy of this diagram, show how the shaded shape will tessellate.

You should draw at least another six shapes.

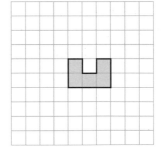

3 On a copy of this diagram, show how the shaded shape will tessellate.

You should draw at least six shapes.

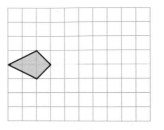

(1387 November 2004)

4 Here is a 6-sided polygon.

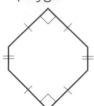

a Write down the mathematical name for a 6-sided polygon.

The angles of the polygon are four angles of 135° and two angles of 90°. The angles of 90° are shown.

This shape tessellates.

b Show in a diagram how the shape tessellates.

Chapter 6
Directed Numbers

Exercise 6A

1 Put these temperatures in order. Start with the lowest temperature.

a   −4°C   2°C   1°C   5°C   4°C

b   3°C   −5°C   4°C   6°C   −3°C

c   0°C   −2°C   −3°C   −1°C   −4°C

2 Put these directed numbers in order. Start with the smallest directed number.

a   −3   3   2   1   4

b   4   −3   2   −1   3

c   0   −3   −1   −5   −2

3 At midnight the temperature was −3°C. By 8 o'clock the next morning the temperature had risen to 4°C. By how many degrees had the temperature risen between midnight and 8 o'clock?

4 The temperature inside a freezer is −6°C. The temperature outside the freezer is 10°C. How many degrees higher is the temperature outside the freezer than the temperature inside?

5 The table shows the temperature at midnight in 4 cities on the same night.

City	Temperature (°C)
Belfast	3
Cardiff	−1
Edinburgh	−4
London	0

a Write down the name of the city which had the lowest temperature.

b Put the temperatures in order. Start with the lowest.

c Work out the difference in temperature between Edinburgh and Belfast.

6 The table shows the highest and lowest temperatures recorded in each of 5 continents in the last 100 years.

Continent	Lowest Temperature (°C)	Highest Temperature (°C)
Africa	−24	58
Asia	−70	54
Australia	−23	53
Europe	−55	50
North America	−63	57

a Which continent had the lowest temperature?

b Which continent had the highest temperature?

c Which continent had the greatest difference between the lowest and highest temperatures?

d For South America the lowest temperature was 9°C lower than the lowest temperature in Africa. Find the lowest temperature in South America.

e The highest temperature in South America is 104°C higher than the lowest temperature in Europe. Find the highest temperature in South America.

7 Use a number line to work out

   a $-4 + 5$ **b** $-4 + 4$

   c $4 - 5$ **d** $-4 - 5$

   e $0 - 8$ **f** $-5 + 2$

   g $-3 - 4 - 7$

8 Copy and complete the following by using a number line to find the missing numbers.

   a $-3 + ? = -1$ **b** $-3 + ? = 4$

   c $-4 - ? = -6$ **d** $6 - ? = -1$

9 Copy and complete the following by using a number line to find the missing numbers.

   a $? - 5 = 2$ **b** $? - 4 = -1$

   c $? + 5 = 2$ **d** $? - 2 = -4$

   e $? + 3 = -4$ **f** $? - 3 = -3$

Exercise 6B

1 Work out

   a $(-4) + (+3)$ **b** $(+4) + (+2)$

   c $(-4) + (-3)$ **d** $(+4) + (-3)$

   e $(-4) + (-3)$ **f** $(-6) + (+2)$

   g $(-4) + (+2)$ **h** $(+3) + (-3)$

2 Work out

   a $(-4) - (+3)$ **b** $(+4) - (-3)$

   c $(-8) - (+2)$ **d** $(-1) - (+4)$

   e $(-5) - (-3)$ **f** $(-2) - (+3)$

   g $(+5) - (-4)$ **h** $(+4) - (+7)$

3 Find the missing directed number.

   a $(-4) - (\ ) = (+4)$

   b $(+3) - (\ ) = (-2)$

   c $(+4) - (\ ) = (+2)$

   d $(\ 1) \ (\ ) = (\ 14)$

   e $(-5) - (\ ) = (-4)$

   f $(-3) - (\ ) = (-4)$

4 Find the missing directed number.

   a $(\ ) - (-3) = (+4)$

   b $(\ ) - (-2) = (+5)$

   c $(\ ) - (+3) = (+1)$

   d $(\ ) - (-5) = (+3)$

   e $(\ ) - (+2) = (-4)$

   f $(\ ) + (-3) = (-4)$

   g $(\ ) + (+2) = (+5)$

   h $(\ ) + (+3) = (-2)$

   i $(\ ) + (-3) = (+4)$

5 Work out

   a $-5 + 1$ **b** $-5 - 3$

   c $-7 + 5$ **d** $5 - 8$

   e $-3 - 4$ **f** $-5 - 3 - 3$

   g $-4 + 2 - 3$ **h** $4 - 7 + 2$

   i $-4 - 2 - 5$

6 Work out

   a $-15 + 12$ **b** $-11 + 16$

   c $23 - 38$ **d** $36 - 54$

   e $-21 - 18$ **f** $-28 - 47$

   g $-23 - 23$ **h** $-12 + 13 - 18$

7 Work out the sum of

   a (-5) and (-3) **b** $(+5)$ and (-2)

   c (-2) and $(+7)$ **d** 4 and -7

   e   5 and -9

Exercise 6C

1 Work out

   a $(+2) \times (-5)$ **b** $(-5) \times (-5)$

   c $(+4) \times (+3)$ **d** $(+12) \times (-4)$

   e $(-6) \times (-3)$ **f** $(-5) \times (-7)$

   g $(-10) \times (-10)$ **h** $(-6) \times (+3)$

2 Work out

   a $(+8) \div (-4)$ **b** $(+18) \div (-3)$

   c $(+9) \div (-3)$ **d** $(+28) \div (+7)$

   e $(-20) \div (-5)$ **f** $(-18) \div (-2)$

   g $(+38) \div (-2)$ **h** $(-16) \div (+4)$

3 Find the missing directed number
  a $(+6) \times (\ ) = (-18)$
  b $(+4) \times (\ ) = (-24)$
  c $(-25) \div (\ ) = (-5)$
  d $(+16) \div (\ ) = (-2)$
  e $(\ ) \times (-5) = (+30)$
  f $(\ ) \times (+6) = (-36)$
  g $(+28) \div (\ ) = (+4)$
  h $(\ ) \times (+7) = (-49)$

4 Work out the product of
  a (-4) and $(+4)$
  b (-5) and $(+6)$
  c $(+4)$ and $(+7)$
  d (-6) and (-7)
  e (-4) and (-8)
  f $(+6)$ and $(+10)$
  g $(+6)$ and (-3)
  h (-5) and (-8)

Exercise 6D

1 Use a calculator to work out
  a $(+4.4) \times (-4.8)$
  b $(-14.8) - (-16.9)$
  c $(+13.5) \div (-2.25)$
  d $(-2.4) \times (-6.4)$
  e $(+14.4) + (-54.8)$
  f $(+54.4) - (-43.8)$

2 Use a calculator to find the missing directed number.
  a $(+3.5) \div (\ ) = (-2.5)$
  b $(+12.4) \times (\ ) = (-31)$
  c $(\ ) \times (-4.5) = (+37.8)$
  d $(+32.7) + (\ ) = (-31.1)$
  e $(-23.4 + (\ ) = (-16.3)$
  f $(-22.4) - (\ ) = (-41)$
  g $(\ ) \div (-2.4) = (-21)$
  h $(-18.9) \div (\ ) = (+12.6)$

3 Use a calculator to work out
  a $\dfrac{4.75 \times (-12.5)}{(-2.5)}$

  b $\dfrac{(-5.4) \times (-7.5)}{(+4.5)}$

  c $\dfrac{(+15.8) \times (-2.4)}{(-9.6)}$

  d $\dfrac{(-12.5)}{(-2.5) - (+2.5)}$

  e $\dfrac{(-12.5)}{(-2.5) \times (+2.5)}$

  f $\dfrac{(+24.4)}{(-2.5)} - (-14.8)$

Chapter 7
Decimals

Exercise 7A

1 Round these to the nearest whole number.
  a 6.3   **b** 8.6   **c** 3.5
  d 14.9   **e** 28.3   **f** 29.9

2 Round these to the nearest whole number.
  a 3.48   **b** 9.82   **c** 7.51
  d 23.63   **e** 85.298   **f** 42.901

3 Round these to the nearest pound (£).
  a £2.36   **b** £6.78   **c** £35.07
  d £15.99   **e** £324.56   **f** £699.99

4 Round these to the nearest metre (m).
  a 2.83 m   **b** 7.83 m   **c** 9.51m
  d 24.67m   **e** 38.01m   **f** 125.29 m

5 Round these to the nearest kilometre (km).
  a 8.13 km   **b** 6.09 km   **c** 1.675 km
  d 79.5 km   **e** 0.625 km   **f** 259.51 km

6 Round these to the nearest kilogram (kg).

   a 1.5 kg   **b** 72.43 kg

   c 9.195 kg   **d** 54.49 kg

   e 106.785 kg   **f** 3.089 kg

Exercise 7B

1 Work out an estimate for

   a 3.1×4.9 **b** 9.8×5.4

   c $12.4 \div 3.01$ **d** 1.83×7.42

   e $39.51 \div 4.09$ **f** 9.21×3.98

2 Work out an estimate for the cost of

   a 4 notebooks at £1.99 each

   b 3 magazines at £2.85 each

   c 5 CDs at £8.75 each

   d 9 pens at £1.24 each

3 Pete bought

     4 packs of nails at £1.85 each

     2 tins of paint at £8.24 each

     1 paint brush at £2.95

  Work out an estimate for the total amount of money that Pete spent.

4 A group of 7 people go to a museum. Tickets cost £6.25 each. Work out an estimate for the total cost of the tickets.

5 Pens cost £3.85 each. Work out an estimate for the total number of pens that can be bought for £20

6 Toy cars cost £1.65 each. Work out an estimate for the number of toy cars that can be bought for £20

7 Susan wants to buy 4 magazines that cost £3.65 each. She has £12

  Does she have enough money to buy the 4 magazines? Give a reason for your answer.

8 A family of 2 adults and 4 children go to the zoo. Adult tickets cost £8.25 and child tickets cost £5.85. Work out an estimate for the total cost of all 6 tickets.

Exercise 7C

1 Work out

   a $8.3 + 6.5$ **b** $3.65 + 2.84$

   c $56.39 + 7.06$ **d** $15.4 + 3.78$

   e $8 + 2.74 + 0.9$ **f** $16.5 + 8.64 + 2.347$

2 Work out

   a $9.48 - 3.16$ **b** $24.52 - 12.36$

   c $86.4 - 13.27$ **d** $17 - 6.8$

   e $65 - 31.46$ **f** $87.2 - 19.63$

3 Work out $7.6 - 4.83$

                (1388 January 2005)

4 A piece of ribbon measures 7.5m. Sarah cuts 2.75m from the piece of ribbon. Work out the length of ribbon left.

5 Jerry buys a train ticket costing £5.40 and a magazine costing £1.85. He pays with a £10 note. Work out how much change Jerry gets.

6 A plank of wood is 3.5 m long. Hal saws off a piece that measures 1.65 m. Jack saws off another piece that measures 0.9 m. Work out the length of wood that is left.

7 Three children pick some strawberries. Jamil picks 3.5 kg, Sahil picks 2.8 kg and Asha picks 1.65 kg of strawberries. Work out the total weight of the strawberries that the children pick.

Exercise 7D

1 Work out

   a 6.7×10 **b** 9.13×10

   c 73.24×10 **d** 0.32×10

   e 0.047×10 **f** 3.04×10

2 Work out

   a 2.37×100 **b** 9.2×100

   c 0.0345×100 **d** 0.8×100

   e 62.1×100 **f** 0.07×100

3 Work out
  a 8.367×1000
  b 4.29×1000
  c 0.082×1000
  d 89.3×1000
  e 0.00306×1000
  f 2.3×1000

4 Work out
  a 7.24×10
  b 82.546×100
  c 13.2×100
  d 53.2×1000
  e 0.0031×10
  f 0.087×1000
  g 0.9×100
  h 0.00395×1000

5 Work out the missing number
  a $23.56 \times ? = 2356$
  b $6.7 \times ? = 67$
  c $0.087 \times ? = 87$
  d $0.76 \times ? = 7.6$
  e $0.04 \times ? = 40$
  f $56.7 \times ? = 5670$
  g $7.123 \times ? = 7123$
  h $0.034 \times ? = 0.34$

6 Work out the cost of
  a 10 pens at £0.23 each
  b 100 newspapers at £1.25 each
  c 10 bottles of drink at £1.05 each
  d 100 calculators at £5.49 each

Exercise 7E

1 Work out
  a 5.3×2 **b** 6.3×4 **c** 9.2×3
  d 8.7×5 **e** 12.6×3 **f** 20.5×5

2 Work out the cost of
  a 2 books at £6.95 each
  b 5 bowls at £3.80 each
  c 4 DVDs at £7.35 each
  d 3 pictures at £8.75 each

3 A folder costs £1.89
  Lesley buys 5 of these folders.
  a Work out an estimate for the total cost.
  b Work out the exact total cost.

4 A computer game costs £8.29
  Ben buys 3 of these computer games.
  a Work out an estimate for the total cost.
  b Work out the exact total cost.

5 Work out
  a 2.53×0.3
  b 7.32×0.2
  c 5.63×0.4
  d 8.04×0.6
  e 5.19×0.05
  f 6.34×0.03

6 Work out
  a 5.3×2.1
  b 7.2×1.3
  c 6.3×0.52
  d 0.34×0.52
  e 9.5×4.3
  f 0.76×5.3

7 The cost of a calculator is £6.79
  Work out the cost of 28 of these calculators.
  (1387 June 2005)

8 Nick takes 26 boxes out of his van.
  The weight of each box is 32.9kg.
  Work out the **total** weight of the 26 boxes.
  (1387 June 2004)

Exercise 7F

1 Work out
  a $56.4 \div 10$
  b $768 \div 10$
  c $0.048 \div 10$
  d $8 \div 10$

2 Work out
  a $451.6 \div 100$
  b $34 \div 100$
  c $6.2 \div 100$
  d $0.56 \div 100$

3 Work out
  a $4356.3 \div 1000$
  b $598 \div 1000$
  c $70.9 \div 1000$
  d $0.34 \div 1000$

4 Work out
  a $34 \div 10$
  b $45.6 \div 100$
  c $83 \div 100$
  d $5.3 \div 1000$
  e $0.45 \div 10$
  f $235.7 \div 100$
  g $36 \div 1000$
  h $0.4 \div 10$

5 Write down the missing number.
  a $8.3 \div ? = 0.83$
  b $29 \div ? = 0.029$
  c $6723 \div ? = 67.23$
  d $54 \div ? = 0.054$
  e $0.78 \div ? = 0.0078$
  f $310 \div ? = 3.1$
  g $5.8 \div ? = 0.0058$
  h $7 \div ? = 0.007$

6 Work out

   a 6.9 × 10   **b** 78.3 ÷ 100

   c 0.0562 × 100 **d** 8.452 ÷ 1000

   e 9.1 × 1000   **f** 0.0406 × 100

   g 89.3 ÷ 10   **h** 0.04 × 100

   i 63 ÷ 1000   **j** 4.065 × 100

   k 4.2 × 100   **l** 3 ÷ 1000

Exercise 7G

1 Work out

   a 86.4 ÷ 2   **b** 4.35 ÷ 5

   c 7.14 ∶ 3   **d** 53.56 ÷ 4

   e 6.7 ÷ 2   **f** 2.34 ÷ 5

   g 0.417 ÷ 3   **h** 18.72 ÷ 6

2 Work out

   a 46 ÷ 0.2   **b** 8.4 ÷ 0.3

   c 3.12 ÷ 0.04 **d** 87.5 ÷ 0.05

   e 8 ÷ 0.02   **f** 0.085 ÷ 0.05

3 Three shirts cost £25.80
Work out the price of one shirt.

4 Five drinks cost £6.75
Work out the price of one drink.

5 Four friends share the cost of a restaurant bill. The bill came to a total of £90.56
Work out how much each person pays.

6 Ali has a piece of ribbon of length 3.4 m. She cuts it up into 4 equal pieces. Work out the length of each piece.

7 Six people share a lottery win of £1443.12 equally. Work out how much money each person will get.

8 A 5 kg bag of peanuts is divided up into smaller bags each containing 0.2 kg of peanuts. Work out the number of smaller bags that can be filled.

Exercise 7H

1 Work out the estimate for the cost of

   a 32 videos at £3.85 each

   b 185 pens at £0.42 each

   c 48 train tickets at £4.20 each

   d 95 calculators at £6.95 each

2 a Round 64.2 to the nearest ten

   b Round 0.34 to one decimal place

   c Use your answers to **a** and **b** to work out an estimate for 64.2 × 0.34

3 Work out an estimate for

   a 47.1 × 0.41   **b** 198 × 3.9

   c 783 ÷ 1.92   **d** 92.3 ÷ 0.027

   e 0.029 × 0.412 **f** 213 ÷ 0.051

4 Work out an estimate for $\dfrac{6.52 \times 0.39}{1.8}$

5 Work out an estimate for $\dfrac{576}{29.6 \times 2.31}$

6 Work out an estimate for the cost of 47 litres of petrol costing 91.3p per litre.

7 Work out an estimate for the value of $\dfrac{5.79 \times 312}{0.523}$

(1387 November 2005)

8 Work out an estimate for the value of $\dfrac{637}{3.2 \times 9.8}$

(1387 June 2005)

Exercise 7I

1 Round these numbers to 1 decimal place

   a 6.78   **b** 32.145   **c** 0.873

   d 19.53   **e** 8.95   **f** 45.609

2 Round these numbers to two decimal places

   a 82.146 **b** 5.674   **c** 0.9847

   d 78.236 **e** 0.0816 **f** 3.4072

3 Round these number to three decimal places

   a 5.2874   **b** 0.06718   **c** 36.9696

   d 3.45167   **e** 0.00462   **f** 0.0295

4 Round these to the number of decimal places given in the brackets

   a 3.28 (1)   **b** 6.4387 (2)

   c 0.519 (1)   **d** 0.04517 (3)

   e 23.914 (2)   **f** 103.26 (1)

   g 0.0348 (2)   **h** 0.09265 (3)

   i 49.95 (1)   **j** 2.675 (2)

   k 12.083 (1)   **l** 0.00417 (3)

5 Use your calculator to work out the value of the following. Give each answer correct to one decimal place.

   a $89.1 \div 0.13$

   b $(67.8 + 9.45) \times 7.62$

   c 56.12×0.48

   d $\dfrac{45.8}{1.2 \times 6.3}$

Exercise 7J

1 Round these numbers to one significant figure

   a 563   **b** 8924   **c** 611

   d 24   **e** 0.0546   **f** 0.00319

2 Round these numbers to three significant figures

   a 5613   **b** 34.186   **c** 0.98134

   d 35.468   **e** 3.1709   **f** 0.0091456

3 Round these to the number of significant figures given in the brackets

   a 923 (1)   **b** 67.354 (3)

   c 128 (2)   **d** 0.0345 (1)

   e 0.03762 (2)   **f** 839 524 (3)

   g 0.00263 (1)   **h** 0.85625 (3)

   i 297 600 (2)   **j** 3.247 (3)

   k 43.73 (2)   **l** 7356 (1)

4 Use your calculator to work out the value of the following. Give each answer correct to 3 significant figures.

   a $6782 \div 43$ **b** 561×29

   c 0.034×0.457 **d** $\dfrac{45.1 \times 63.6}{0.09}$

   e $\dfrac{45.21}{67.2 - 7.93}$ **f** $\dfrac{73.51 + 26.3}{5.34 - 2.9}$

5 a Write the number 56 392 correct to one significant figure.

   b Write the number 0.0436 correct to one significant figure.   *(1388 January 2005)*

6 a Write the number 7623 correct to 1 significant figure.

   b Write the number 0.00821 correct to 2 significant figures.

   c Use your calculator to work out

     $\dfrac{15.1 + 4.82}{6.2 - 3.7}$

    Write down all the figures on your calculator display.

                   (1388 November 2005)

Exercise 7K

1 Steve works for 43 hours in one week. He is paid £8.75 per hour. Work out Steve's pay for the week.

2 For each journey a taxi firm charges £2.40 for the first mile of the journey and £1.38 for each **extra** mile. Work out how much the taxi firm charges for a 6 mile journey.

3 Josie buys stamps at 32p each. She pays with a £5 note. Work out the greatest number of 32p stamps Josie can buy.

4 Harry works for 14 hours. He is paid £8.70 per hour for the first 8 hours. For the remaining hours he is paid £13.05 per hour. Work out the total amount that Harry is paid.

5 A bar of chocolate costs 92p.
Peter buys four of these bars.
He pays with a £5 note.
Work out how much change he should get.
(1388 March 2005)

6 Rizwan buys
    6 stamps at 25p each
    2 packs of postcards at 89p per pack
    1 pack of labels at £1.09
He pays with a £10 note.
Work out how much change Rizwan should get.
(1388 November 2005)

7 Farah buys
    2 pens at 84p each
    3 folders at £1.35 each
    1 pencil case at £1.49
She pays with a £10 note.
Work out how much change Farah should get from £10
(1388 January 2003)

8 Mr Holland uses 367 units of electricity in one month.
He pays 5.84p for each unit of electricity.
Mr Holland also pays a fixed charge of £6.14 for the month.
Work out the **total amount** he pays.
(1388 March 2003)

9 Alex has a mobile phone.
Each month he pays
    13.4p for each minute he uses his mobile phone
    and
    a fixed charge of £18.75
In January Alex uses his mobile phone for 405 minutes.
Work out the **total amount** Alex pays.
(1388 March 2005)

Chapter 8
Algebra 1

Exercise 8A

1 Write these as simply as possible
  a $3 \times d$ **b** $y \times 5$

  c $p + p + p + p$
  d $q + q + q + q + q + q + q$

2 There are n coins in a bag. John puts six more coins into the bag. How many coins are now in the bag?

3 There are x people on a train. Forty people get off the train. How many people are now on the train?

4 There are c cats. Each cat has 4 legs. What is the total number of legs?

5 Janine buys 13 CDs. Each CD costs p pounds. Find, in terms of p, the total cost of the 13 CDs.

6 There are x students in a class. 12 of the students are girls.
  a Find, in terms of x, the number of students that are boys.
  3 girls and 2 boys leave the class.
  b Find, in terms of x, the number of
    i students now in the class
    ii boys now in the class.

7 There are 20 rows of seats in a cinema.
In each row there are y seats.
7 seats in the cinema are broken.
Find, in terms of y, the total number of seats in the cinema that are **not** broken.

Exercise 8B

1 There are b black socks and w white socks in a drawer.
Write down an expression, in terms of b and w, for the total number of socks in the drawer.

2 There are m children in a room. n children are seated and the rest are standing. Write down an expression, in terms of m and n, for the number of children standing.

3 There are 5 biscuits in each packet. Maria buys y packets of biscuits and then eats b biscuits. Write down an expression, in terms of y and b, for the total number of biscuits Maria has left.

4 In football matches 3 points are awarded for a win, 1 point is awarded for a draw and no points are awarded for a loss. Jim's football team will play 20 matches next year. He expects his team to win p of them, draw q of them and lose the rest of the matches. Write down an expression, in terms of p and q, for

    a the total number of matches Jim expects his team to lose next year

    b the total number of points Jim expects his team to be awarded next year.

5 Work out the value of each of these expressions when $x = 3$, $y = 4$ and $z = 10$

    a $5x$ **b** $y + 7$

    c $z - 6$ **d** $x + y$

    e $z - y$ **f** $x + y + z$

    g $2x + 7$ **h** $3y - 2$

    i $3x + z$ **j** $2z - y$

    k $3x + 2z$ **l** $4x + y + 3$

    m $x + 2y - z$ **n** $5x + 3y - 2z$

Exercise 8C

1 Simplify these expressions by collecting like terms.

    a $6x + 4x$ **b** $7p - 6p$

    c $2q - 5q$ **d** $2y + 3y + 2$

    e $5d + 3 - 3d$ **f** $c + 1 - 2c$

2 Simplify

    a $5x + 2x + 3y + 6y$

    b $4x - x + 7y - 3y$

    c $x + 3y - 2y + 3y$

    d $2x - 3x + 4x - 2x + 4y - 2y$

    e $2x + 7y - 3y + 7x$

    f $x + 6y + 4y - 8y - 4x$

    g $5u + 2p - 5p - 3u$

    h $7k - t - t - 2k$

3 **a** Simplify $q + q + q$

    b Simplify $4r + 5t + 7r - 2t$

                   (1388 March 2006)

4 **a** Simplify $5m + 3m - 2m$

    b Simplify $p + 7q + 3p - 2q$

               (1388 November 2005)

5 Simplify $3a + 7b + 9a - 4b$

                   (1388 March 2006)

6 Simplify

    a $3p + 3q - 4p + q + 2p$

    b $4a + 4d - 5d - a + 4d - 3a$

    c $5x + 3y - 5 + 5y - x + 2$

    d $6s - 7t - 7s + 3s + 3 - 4t + 1$

Exercise 8D

1 Write these expressions in the simplest way

    a $a \times b \times c$ **b** $p \times 5 \times r$

    c $m \times m$ **d** $4s \times t \times u$

    e $x \times x \times x$ **f** $y \times 2 \times y$

    g $p \times p \times 2 \times q$

2 Simplify $4a \times 3b$

                   (1388 November 2005)

3 Simplify

    a $4 \times 3a$ **b** $5p \times 3$

    c $8g \times h$ **d** $y \times 5z$

    e $6s \times 7t$ **f** $8m \times 3n$

    g $5c \times 2 \times 7d$ **h** $3d \times 4e \times 5$

    i $x \times 3x$ **j** $c \times d \times 4e$

    k $2u \times 5v \times w$ **l** $a \times a \times 6a$

    m $5a \times 2b \times a$ **n** $2xy \times 4y$

    o $a \times b + a \times b$ **p** $y \times y + y \times y$

    q $p \times p + p \times p + p \times p$

4 Simplify $pq + pq + pq$

                   (1388 March 2006)

5 $p = 2$. Work out the value of $5p^3$

                   (1388 March 2006)

6 Work out the value of each of these expressions when $x = 2, y = 3, z = 4$

a xy b xyz

c $5xz$ d $yz - 2xy$

e $6xz - 5xy$ f $5x^2$

g $10y^2 + x - z$ h x^3

i $x + y^2$ j $y^3 - yz$

k $5x^3 - xz^2$ l $z^3 - y^3 - x^3$

m $yx^2 + zy^2$

Exercise 8E

1 Multiply out

a $4(x + 1)$ b $2(y + 3)$

c $3(z + 5)$ d $5(1 + k)$

e $2(x - 1)$ f $4(n - 6)$

g $5(m - 7)$ h $3(2 - q)$

i $3(x + y)$ j $5(n + m)$

k $2(p - q)$ l $4(s - t)$

2 Multiply out $3(t - 4)$

(1388 November 2005)

3 Multiply out

a $3(2x + 3)$ b $2(5y - 2)$

c $4(3 + 4z)$ d $5(1 - 3p)$

e $2(3q + 7r)$ f $3(3s - t)$

g $5(5u - 4v)$ h $4(p + 2 + 3q)$

i $6(1 + 2e + f)$ j $5(3r + 2s - 4)$

k $4(2p - 3q - 4r)$

4 Simplify

a $3(z + 2) + 1$

b $5(y + 3) - 3y$

c $4(x + 1) - 7$

d $2(3 + w) - 7w$

e $4(u + v) + 1(u + 3v)$

f $4(2a + 3b) + 3(4a + 3b)$

g $2(4c + 3d) + 4(2c - 3d)$

h $2(2e + 3f) + 3(2f - e)$

i $6(4g - 3h) + 5(3h - 2g)$

Exercise 8F

1 Copy and complete

a $7x + 14 = 7 \times x + 7 \times 2$
$= 7 (.... + ...)$

b $12y + 9 = 3 \times 4y + 3 \times 3$
$= 3 (.... + ...)$

c $8p - 4q - 20r$
$= 4 \times 2p - 4 \times q - 4 \times 5r$
$= 4 (.... - .... - ....)$

2 Factorise

a $5x + 10$ b $9y + 3$

c $35z - 7$ d $33a + 11b$

e $6c + 8d$ f $9e - 15f$

g $12g - 18h$ h $16m + 24n$

i $10p \quad 15q$ j $20r + 24s$

k $8t - 12u + 20$ l $4v - 8w - 10$

m $36x \quad 30y \quad 42z$

3 Factorise $5y + 40$ *(1388 March 2006)*

Chapter 9
Perimeter and area of 2-D shapes

Exercise 9A

1 A shaded shape has been drawn on a grid of centimetre squares. Find the perimeter of the shaded shape.

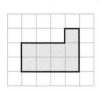

(1388 April 2006)

2 Work out the perimeter of these rectangles

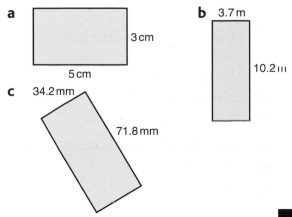

a — 5 cm, 3 cm

b — 3.7 m, 10.2 m

c — 34.2 mm, 71.8 mm

3 Work out the perimeter of
  a an equilateral triangle of side 15 cm
  b a regular pentagon of side 12 cm.

4 The diagram shows a shape.
The shape is an 8-sided polygon.

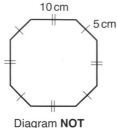

10 cm

5 cm

Diagram **NOT** accurately drawn

  a Write down the mathematical name for an 8-sided polygon.

The diagram shows the lengths of two of the sides of the shape.

  b Work out the perimeter of the shape.
              (5540 June 2005)

5 A square has a perimeter of 72 cm. Work out the length of each side of the square.

6 The diagram shows a shape. All the corners of the shape are right angles.
Work out the perimeter of the shape.

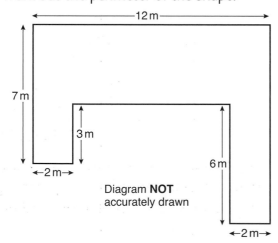

←—————12 m—————→

7 m

3 m

←2 m→

6 m

←2 m→

Diagram **NOT** accurately drawn

Exercise 9B

1 Find the area, in cm², of the shape.

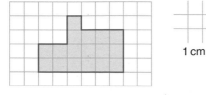

1 cm

1 cm

(1385 June 1996)

2 Here are 8 shapes on a grid of centimetre squares.

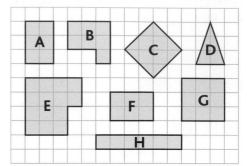

A   B   C   D
E   F   G
H

  a Find the area of shape **C**.
  b Write down the special name for triangle **D**.

Two of the shapes are congruent.

  c Write down the letter of these two shapes.
              (1388 November 2005)

  d Find the perimeter of shape
      i A   ii B   iii F   iv H
  e Find the area of shape   **i E   ii G**

3 A shape has been drawn on a grid of centimetre squares.

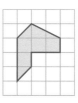

Work out the area of the shape.
State the units with your answer.
              (1387 June 2005)

4 A shape is shown on a centimetre grid.
Find an estimate for the area of the shape.

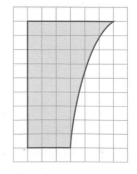

Exercise 9C

1 Find the areas of these rectangles and squares.

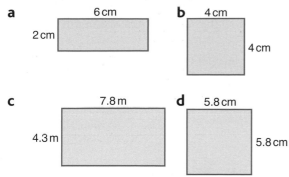

a 6 cm, 2 cm

b 4 cm, 4 cm

c 7.8 m, 4.3 m

d 5.8 cm, 5.8 cm

2 Work out the areas of these triangles.

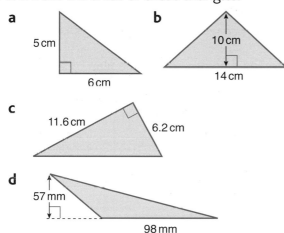

a 5 cm, 6 cm

b 10 cm, 14 cm

c 11.6 cm, 6.2 cm

d 57 mm, 98 mm

3 Work out the area of the triangle. Give the units with your answer.

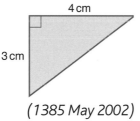

4 cm, 3 cm

(1385 May 2002)

4 a Work out the area of these shapes drawn on a centimetre grid.

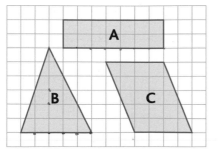

A   B   C

b On centimetre squared paper, draw a rectangle with area 24 cm².

5 Work out the areas of these parallelograms.

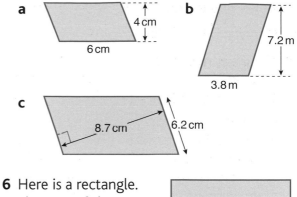

a 4 cm, 6 cm

b 7.2 m, 3.8 m

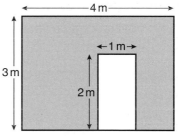

c 8.7 cm, 6.2 cm

6 Here is a rectangle. The area of the rectangle is 63 cm². The length of the rectangle is 9 cm.

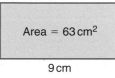

Area = 63 cm², 9 cm

a Work out the breadth of the rectangle.

b Work out the perimeter of the rectangle.

Exercise 9D

1 The diagram shows a wall with a door in it. Work out the shaded area.

4 m, 3 m, 1 m, 2 m

(1387 June 2005)

2 The diagram shows a 6-sided shape made from a rectangle and a right-angled triangle. Work out the total area of the 6-sided shape.

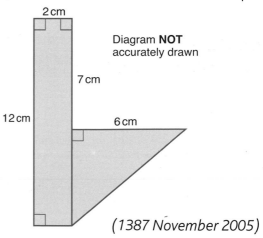

2 cm, 7 cm, 12 cm, 6 cm

Diagram **NOT** accurately drawn

(1387 November 2005)

3 *ABCD* is a trapezium.
Angle *A* = 90°.
Angle *D* = 90°.
AB = 7 cm. *AD* = 8 cm. *DC* = 13 cm.
Work out the area of the trapezium.

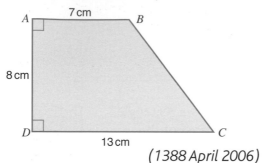

(1388 April 2006)

4 A rectangular lawn is 18 m by 16 m.
  a Work out the area of the lawn.
Alan wants to buy some lawn food for this lawn.
A box of lawn food covers 100 m² of lawn.
  b How many boxes of lawn food does Alan need to buy to feed this lawn once?
The cost of a box of lawn food is £9.99
  c Work out how much these boxes of lawn food will cost Alan.

5 The diagram shows a 5 m by 4 m rectangular pond.
There is a path of width 1 m around the pond.

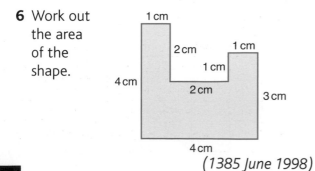

The inner edge of the path is a 5 m by 4 m rectangle.
  a What are the dimensions of the rectangle that is the outer edge of the path?
  b Work out the area of the path.

6 Work out the area of the shape.

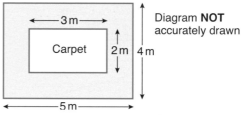

(1385 June 1998)

7 A floor is a 5 m by 3.5 m rectangle. Carpet tiles, which are squares of side 50 cm, are used to carpet the floor. Work out how many carpet tiles are needed.

8 The length of each diagonal of a square is 20 cm.
Work out the area of the square.

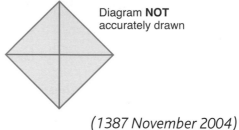

Diagram **NOT** accurately drawn

(1387 November 2004)

9 The diagram shows the plan of a floor.
There is a carpet in the middle of the floor.
Work out the shaded area.

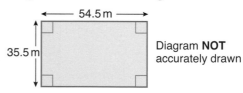

Diagram **NOT** accurately drawn

(5540 June 2005)

10 The diagram shows a rectangular field.

Diagram **NOT** accurately drawn

The length of the field is 54.5 m.
The width of the field is 35.5 m.
The field is for sale.
Mrs Fox wants to buy the field.
She also wants to plant a hedge along the perimeter.
The field costs £11.44 per square metre.
Each metre of hedge costs £4.81.
Mrs Fox has £23 000
Has Mrs Fox enough money to buy the field and plant the hedge?
You must show the working you use to make your decision. *(1387 November 2005)*

Exercise 9E

1 Change 8560 mm² to cm². *(1387 June 2004)*

2 Change 1520 cm² to m².

3 Change 50 000 mm² to cm².
(1387 November 2005)

4 Change 7 m² to cm². *(1387 June 2005)*

5 Change to cm²
  a 8.4 m²   **b** 834 mm²

6 Change to mm²
  a 21 cm²   **b** 5.2 m²

7 Change to m²
  a 360 000 cm²   **b** 5 km²

8 A rectangle measures 8.3 cm by 45 mm.
Find the area of the rectangle in
  i cm²   **ii** mm².

9 Work out the area of this triangle in
  i m²   **ii** cm².

2.6 m

180 cm

Chapter 10
Sequences

Exercise 10A

1 Here is a sequence of patterns made up of crosses.

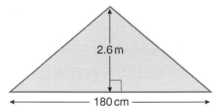

Pattern 1   Pattern 2   Pattern 3   Pattern 4

  a Write down the rule for this sequence.

b Draw Pattern 5

c Complete the table

Pattern number	1	2	3	4	5	6
Number of crosses	3	5	7	9		

d Write down the number of crosses in Pattern 9

2 Here is a sequence of patterns made up of crosses.

× × ×
× × ×
         × × ×   × × ×
         × × ×   × × ×
  × × ×   × × ×   × × ×
  × × ×   × × ×   × × ×
× × ×   × × ×   × × ×   × × ×

Pattern 1   Pattern 2   Pattern 3   Pattern 4

  a Write down the rule for this sequence.

  b Draw Pattern 5.

  c Copy and complete the table

Pattern number	1	2	3	4	5	6
Number of crosses	3	9	15	21		

  d Write down the number of crosses in Pattern 8

3 Here is a sequence of patterns made up of black dots and white dots.

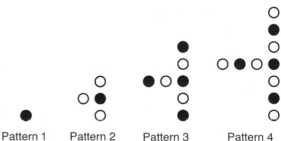

Pattern 1   Pattern 2   Pattern 3   Pattern 4

  a Draw Pattern 5

  b Copy and complete the table.

Pattern number	1	2	3	4	5	6
Number of black dots	1	1	4	4		
Number of white dots	0	3	3	6		
Total number of dots	1	4	7	10		

  c Write down the total number of dots in Pattern 9

4 Here are the first four numbers of a simple sequence.

$$6 \quad 10 \quad 14 \quad 18$$

Write down the next two numbers in the sequence. *(1388 January 2004)*

5 Here are the first five terms of a number sequence.

$$360 \quad 353 \quad 346 \quad 339 \quad 332$$

Write down the next two terms of the number sequence.

6 Here are the first five terms of a number sequence.

$$3 \quad 8 \quad 13 \quad 18 \quad 23$$

  a Write down the next **two** terms of the sequence.

  b Explain how you found your answer.

  c Explain why 387 is **not** a term of the sequence. *(1387 June 2004)*

7 Here is a sequence of numbers.

$$8, \quad 12, \quad 16, \quad 20, \quad 24, \dots$$

  a Write down the 4th term.

  b Write down the rule for this sequence.

  c Write down the next two terms of this sequence.

  d Work out the 10th term of this sequence.

8 Write down the 3rd, 4th and 5th terms of each of these sequences.

  a 5, 10, … , … , … , 30, 35

  b 5, 10, … , … , … , 160, 320

9 Here are the first four terms of a sequence of numbers.

$$24 \quad 29 \quad 34 \quad 39$$

  a Write down the next two terms of the sequence.

  b Write down the rule for the sequence.

  c Write down the 10th term of this sequence.

  d Pat says that 292 is not a term of the sequence. Explain why Pat is correct.

10 Here are the first five terms of a sequence of numbers.

$$19 \quad 21 \quad 23 \quad 25 \quad 27$$

  a Work out the 12th term of the sequence.

  b Explain why 98 is not a term of the sequence.

  c Write down a number that is greater than 200 and is a term of the sequence.

11 Here is a sequence of numbers.

$$48, \quad 42, \quad 36, \quad 30, \quad 24, \dots$$

  a Write down the rule for this sequence.

  b Work out the 8th term of this sequence

  c Which term in this sequence is -42?

  d Explain why -137 is not a term of the sequence.

  e Preety adds the first 17 terms of the sequence. What answer should she get?

Exercise 10B

1 **a** Write down the inverse of -8

  b Write down the inverse of $\div 2$

  c Write down the inverse of $+1$

  d Write down the inverse of $\times 20$

Questions **2–5** show a table for an input and output machine. For each question, copy and complete the table.

2

+6	
Input	**Output**
1	7
2	………
3	………
………	12
………	17
n	………

3

×7	
Input	Output
2	....
3	....
5	....
....	49
....	63
n	....

4

÷4	
Input	Output
4	....
8	....
....	4
....	10
....	12
....	$8n$

5

$-y$	
Input	Output
4	....
5	....
n	....
....	$7 - y$
....	$4y$

Exercise 10C

 Questions **1–5** show tables for input and output machines. The tables are incomplete. Copy and complete each table.

1

×5 −4	
Input	Output
1	1
2	....
4	....
....	11
....	41
n	....

2

×(−2) +25	
Input	Output
1	23
2	....
4	....
....	7
....	1
n	....

3

−2 ×3	
Input	Output
1	−3
2	....
5	....
....	12
....	27
n	....

4

+3 ÷2	
Input	Output
1	....
3	....
....	4
....	7
....	11
....	n

5

−2x +3y	
Input	Output
x	....
$2y$	....
$x + y$	....
....	0
....	$3y$
....	$3x + 4y$

Exercise 10D

1 An expression for the nth term of the arithmetic sequence 5, 7, 9, 11, ... is $2n + 3$

   a Find the 10th term of the sequence.

   b Find the 100th term of the sequence.

2 Here are the first five terms of an arithmetic sequence. 1, 3, 5, 7, 9

  a Write down, in terms of n, an expression for the nth term of this sequence.

  b 1 is the first odd number. Find the 100th odd number.

3 The first five terms of an arithmetic sequence are 9, 13, 17, 21, 25
Find, in terms of n, an expression for the nth term of this sequence.

  (1388 March 2006)

4 The first five terms of an arithmetic sequence are 2, 9, 16, 23, 30
Find, in terms of n, an expression for the nth term of this sequence.

  (1388 January 2004)

5 The first four terms of an arithmetic sequence are 71, 74, 77, 80
Find, in terms of n, an expression for the nth term of this sequence.

  (1388 January 2002)

6 Here are the first five terms of an arithmetic sequence. 40, 20, 0, −20, −40

  a Write down, in terms of n, an expression for the nth term of this sequence.

  b Find the 25th term of the sequence.

7 a Write down, in terms of n, an expression for the nth term of the arithmetic sequence 100, 98, 96, 94, ...

  b Write down, in terms of n, an expression for the nth term of the arithmetic sequence 0, −6, −12, −18, ...

  c Use your answers to parts **a** and **b** to find, in terms of n, an expression for the nth term of the arithmetic sequence 100, 92, 84, 76, ...

Chapter 11
Angles 2

Exercise 11A

In Questions **1–6**, find the size of each of the angles marked with letters. Show your working. The diagrams are not accurately drawn.

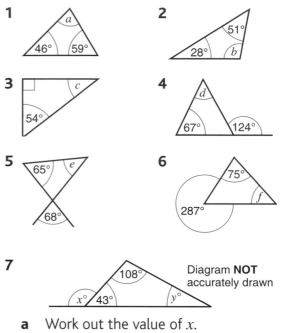

7

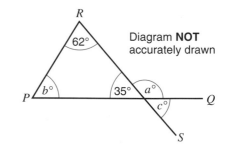

Diagram **NOT** accurately drawn

  a Work out the value of x.

  b Work out the value of y.

  (1388 January 2004)

8

Diagram **NOT** accurately drawn

In the diagram, PQ and RS are straight lines.

  a **i** Work out the value of a.

    ii Give a reason for your answer.

  b **i** Work out the value of b.

    ii Give a reason for your answer.

  c **i** Work out the value of c.

    ii Give a reason for your answer.

  (1385 June 1999)

Exercise 11B

In Questions **1–10**, find the size of each of the angles marked with letters and show your working. The diagrams are not accurately drawn.

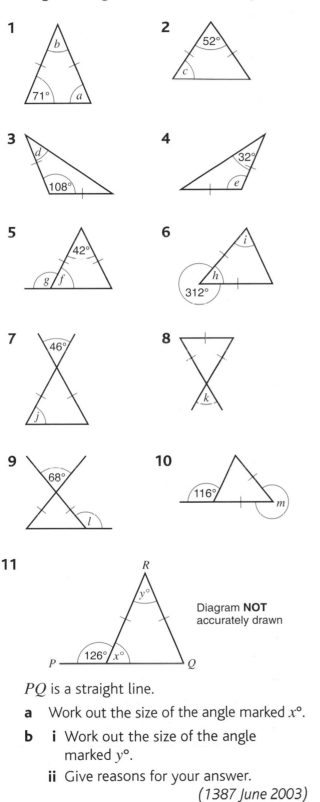

Exercise 11C

In Questions **1–6**, find the size of each of the angles marked with letters and show your working. The diagrams are not accurately drawn.

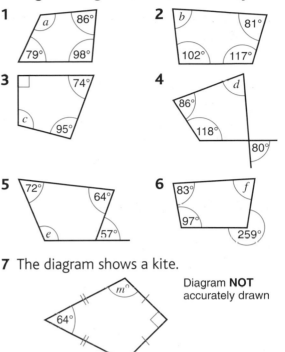

7 The diagram shows a kite.

Diagram **NOT** accurately drawn

Work out the value of *m*.

8 The diagram shows an isosceles trapezium.

Diagram **NOT** accurately drawn

Work out the value of *n*.

11

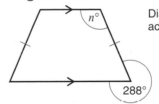

Diagram **NOT** accurately drawn

PQ is a straight line.

a Work out the size of the angle marked *x*°.

b **i** Work out the size of the angle marked *y*°.

ii Give reasons for your answer.

(1387 June 2003)

9

Diagram **NOT** accurately drawn

a **i** Work out the value of *x*.

ii Give a reason for your answer.

b **i** Work out the value of *y*.

ii Give a reason for your answer.

c **i** Work out the value of *z*.

ii Give a reason for your answer.

(1384 November 1997)

10 The diagram shows a kite *ABCD*.

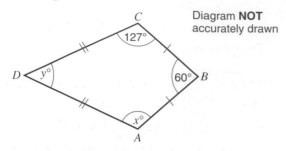

Diagram **NOT** accurately drawn

a **i** Write down the value of *x*.
ii Give a reason for your answer.

b **i** Work out the value of *y*.
ii Give a reason for your answer.

c Show that *ABC* is an equilateral triangle.
(4400 May 2005)

Exercise 11D

In this exercise, the diagrams are not accurately drawn.

1 Find the sum of the angles of a 14-sided polygon.

2 Find the sum of the angles of a 30-sided polygon.

In Questions **3** and **4**, find the size of each of the angles marked with letters and show your working.

3

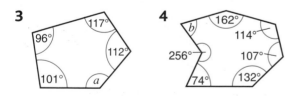

4

5 Work out the size of each interior angle of a regular 18-sided polygon.

6 Work out the size of the angle at the centre of a regular 30-sided polygon.

7 The angle at the centre of a regular polygon is 72°.
How many sides has the polygon?

8 The angle at the centre of a regular polygon is 10°.
a How many sides has the polygon?
b Work out the size of each interior angle of the polygon.

9

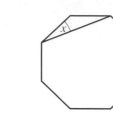

Diagram **NOT** accurately drawn

The diagram shows a regular octagon.
Work out the size of the angle marked *x*.
(1388 November 2005)

10 **a** Work out the size of the angle at the centre of a regular 15-sided polygon.
b Draw a circle with a radius of 5 cm and, using your answer to part **a**, draw a regular 15-sided polygon inside the circle.

11 The diagram shows a pentagon.

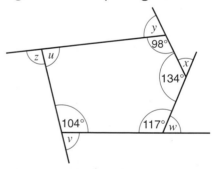

a Work out the size of each of the angles marked with letters.
b Work out *v + w + x + y + z*

12 *ABCDEF* is a regular hexagon with centre *O*.

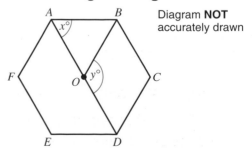

Diagram **NOT** accurately drawn

a What type of triangle is ABO?

b **i** Work out the size of the angle marked $x°$.

  ii Work out the size of the angle marked $y°$.

c **i** What type of quadrilateral is $BCDO$?

  ii Copy this diagram to show how three such quadrilaterals can tessellate to make a hexagon.

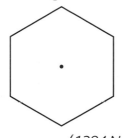

(1384 November 1996)

Exercise 11E

1 At a vertex of a polygon, the size of the interior angle is 107°.
Work out the size of the exterior angle.

2 At a vertex of a polygon, the size of the exterior angle is 54°.
Work out the size of the interior angle.

3 The sizes of three of the exterior angles of a quadrilateral are 93°, 104° and 85°.
Work out the size of the other exterior angle.

4 The size of four of the exterior angles of a pentagon are 57°, 89°, 48° and 112°.
Work out the size of the other exterior angle.

5 Work out the size of each exterior angle of a regular hexagon.

6 Work out the size of each exterior angle of a regular 20-sided polygon.

7 For a regular 45-sided polygon, work out

  a the size of each exterior angle,

  b the size of each interior angle.

8 The size of each exterior angle of a regular polygon is 24°.
Work out the number of sides the polygon has.

9 The size of each interior angle of a regular polygon is 174°. Work out

  a the size of each exterior angle

  b the number of sides the polygon has.

10 Is it possible to have a regular polygon with 27° as the size of each of its exterior angles? Explain your answer.

Exercise 11F

1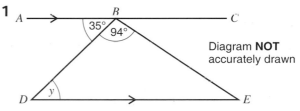

Diagram **NOT** accurately drawn

Find the size of the angle marked y.
Give a reason for your answer.

(1388 March 2002)

2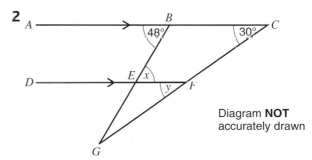

Diagram **NOT** accurately drawn

BEG and CFG are straight lines.
ABC is parallel to DEF.
Angle $ABE = 48°$. Angle $BCF = 30°$.

a **i** Write down the size of the angle marked x.

  ii Give a reason for your answer.

b **i** Write down the size of the angle marked y.

  ii Give a reason for your answer.

(1387 November 2005)

3

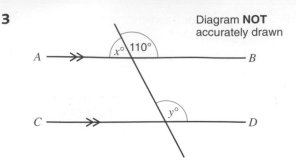

Diagram **NOT** accurately drawn

AB is parallel to *CD*.

a Work out the size of angle *x*°.

b **i** Work out the size of angle *y*°.
ii Give a reason for your answer.

(1388 January 2002)

4

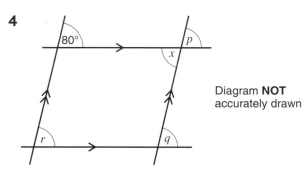

Diagram **NOT** accurately drawn

The diagram has two pairs of parallel lines.
Angles marked *p* and *q* are equal.

a What geometrical name is given to this type of equal angles?

b Write down the size of angle *r*.

c **i** Write down the size of angle *x*.
ii What geometrical name is given to the pair of angles *x* and *q*?

(1384 June 1995)

5

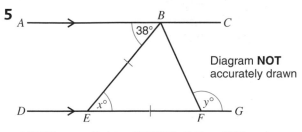

Diagram **NOT** accurately drawn

ABC is parallel to *DEFG*. *BE = EF*.
Angle *ABE* = 38°.

a **i** Find the value of *x*.
ii Give a reason for your answer.

b Work out the value of *y*.

(1388 March 2005)

6

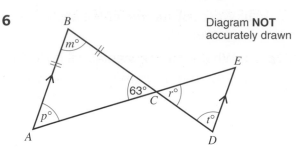

Diagram **NOT** accurately drawn

AB = BC. Angle *ACB* = 63°. *ACE* and *BCD* are straight lines.

a **i** Find the size of the angle marked *p*°.
ii Give a reason for your answer.

b Work out the size of
i the angle marked *m*°
ii the angle marked *r*°.

AB is parallel to *DE*.

c **i** Find the size of the angle marked *t*°.
ii Explain how you worked out your answer.

(1385 November 1999)

7 In the diagram, *PQR* and *PST* are straight lines.
QS and *RT* are parallel lines.
Angle *QRT* = 70°. Angle *QST* = 120°.

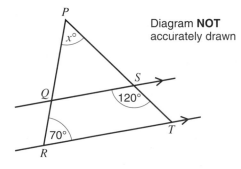

Diagram **NOT** accurately drawn

Work out the value of *x*.
Give a reason for each step in your working.

(4400 May 2005)

Exercise 11G

In this exercise, the diagrams are not accurately drawn.

Find the size of each of the angles marked with letters.

Give reasons for your answers.

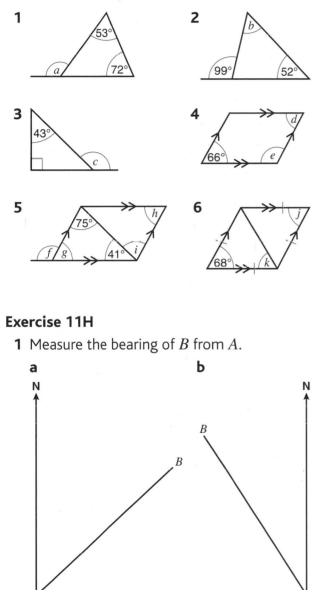

1

2

3

4

5

6

Exercise 11H

1 Measure the bearing of B from A.

a

b

2 Draw diagrams similar to those in Question 1 to show the bearings

   a 073°   **b** 169°   **c** 218°

   d 270°   **e** 329°

3 The diagram is part of a map showing the positions of several cities.

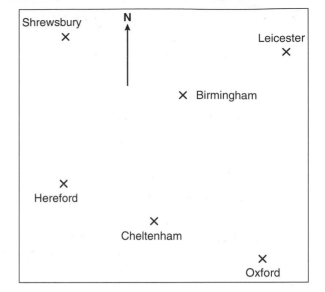

Trace the diagram. Measure and write down the bearing of

   a Leicester from Cheltenham

   b Oxford from Hereford

   c Oxford from Birmingham

   d Hereford from Shrewsbury

   e Leicester from Oxford

   f Cheltenham from Birmingham

   g Shrewsbury from Leicester

   h Birmingham from Oxford

   i Hereford from Birmingham

   j Shrewsbury from Cheltenham.

4 The diagram shows the position of two ships, A and B.
Copy the diagram.
A ship C is on a bearing of 036° from ship A.
Ship C is also on a bearing of 284° from ship B.
Draw an accurate diagram to find the position of ship C.
Mark the position of ship C with a cross **X**.
Label it C.

5

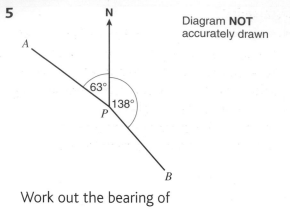

Diagram **NOT** accurately drawn

Work out the bearing of

a A from P

b P from B.

Chapter 12
Graphs 1

Exercise 12A

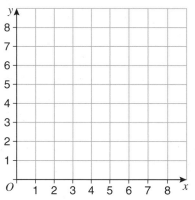

1 Make a copy of the grid and on your grid, plot and label the following points.

a A (2, 3) **b** B (6, 1) **c** C (4, 8)
d D (8, 4) **e** E (5, 0) **f** F (0, 7)

2 Make another copy of the grid.
On your grid, plot the points $P(2, 2)$, $Q(2,5)$, $R(6, 7)$ and $S(6, 4)$. Join the points to form a quadrilateral. Write down the mathematical name of this quadrilateral.

3 The point $S(1, 3)$ is one vertex of a square of side 4 units. Write down the coordinates of the points which form the other three vertices of this square.

Exercise 12B

1 Draw a grid with x and y-axes from -6 to 6, (see p213 of the Student Book) then plot and label the following points.

a A (–2, 4) **b** B (6, –1) **c** C (–3, –5)
d D (–6, 2) **e** E (–1, 6) **f** F (0, –4)

2 $LMNP$ is a rectangle.
L is the point with coordinates (–5, 4),
M is the point with coordinates (–2, 4),
N is the point with coordinates (–2, –1).
Write down the coordinates of the point P.

3 $P(–2, –3)$, $Q(1,–3)$ and $R(5, 2)$ are three vertices of a parallelogram $PQRS$.
Find the coordinates of point S.

Exercise 12C

1 Find the coordinates of the midpoints of the lines joining the following points

a (1, 1) and (3, 1) **b** (1, 1) and (1, 5)
c (1, 1) and (3, 5) **d** (2, 3) and (4, 1)
e (2, 3) and (5, 4)

2 Find the coordinates of the midpoints of the lines joining the following points

a (3, –2) and (3, 6) **b** (3, –2) and (–3, –2)
c (3, –2) and (5, 0) **d** (3, –2) and (–3, 2)
e (3, –2) and (0, 0)

3 A is the point with coordinates (– 5, 2).
B is the point with coordinates (4, 7).
Find the coordinates of the midpoint of AB.

4 The point (3, –1) is the midpoint of the line PQ. The coordinates of P are (1, –3).
Find the coordinates of Q.

Exercise 12D

1 Trevor is paid expenses for each mile he uses his car for work. The following graph shows the amount he is paid for each mile travelled.

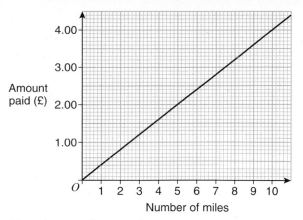

Use the graph to estimate

a the amount he is paid for travelling 6 miles

b the number of miles travelled when he is paid £1.60

c the amount he is paid for travelling 8.5 miles

d the number of miles travelled when he is paid £3.60

e the amount he is paid for travelling 125 miles

f the number of miles travelled when he is paid £60

Exercise 12E

1 The diagram shows a conversion graph between miles and kilometres. Use the graph to change

a i 40 miles to kilometres
  ii 95 miles to kilometres
  iii 500 miles to kilometres

b i 80 kilometres to miles
  ii 110 kilometres to miles
  iii 500 kilometres to miles

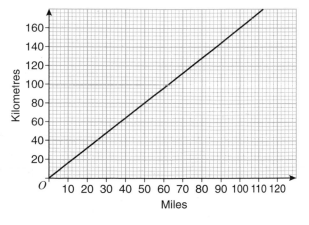

Exercise 12F

1 Robert left school at 3 30 pm. He walked home. On the way home, he stopped to talk to a friend. His sister, Sarah, left the same school at 3 45 pm. She cycled home using the same route as Robert.
Here are the distance-time graphs for Robert's and Sarah's complete journeys.

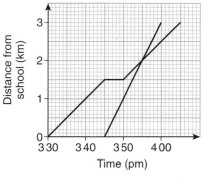

a Find the distance Robert walked during the first 10 minutes of his journey.

b Find the total time that Robert stopped to talk to his friend.

c Write down the distance that Robert had walked when Sarah cycled past him.

(1388 March 2005)

2 Here is part of a travel graph of Siân's journey from her house to the shops and back.

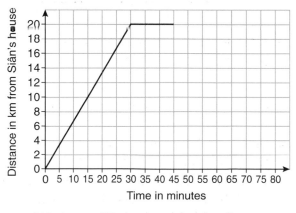

a Work out Siân's speed for the first 30 minutes of her journey.
Give your answer in km/h.

Siân spends 15 minutes at the shops. She then travels back to her house at 60 km/h.

b Complete the travel graph.

(1387 June 2003)

3 The graph shows Becky's journey to see her friend who lives 18 km from Becky's home.

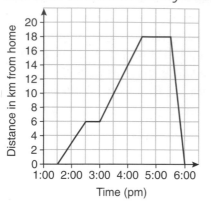

a At what time did Becky arrive at her friend's?

b Becky stopped on the way to see another friend.
  i How is this shown on the graph?
  ii How long did she stop?

c How many minutes did the return journey take?

d Work out the average speed, in kilometres per hour, of each part of Becky's journey.

Chapter 13
Further Fractions

Exercise 13A

1 Find $\frac{1}{7}$ of

a £14	**b** £70	**c** £7
d £21	**e** £28	**f** £56

2 Find

a $\frac{3}{4}$ of 20 cm   **b** $\frac{3}{4}$ of 32 cm

c $\frac{2}{3}$ of 30 kg   **d** $\frac{2}{3}$ of £33

e $\frac{2}{5}$ of 45 km   **f** $\frac{2}{5}$ of 30 litres

g $\frac{3}{4}$ of 124 km   **h** $\frac{4}{5}$ of 175 kg

i $\frac{3}{7}$ of 154 litres   **j** $\frac{5}{8}$ of 128 miles

k $\frac{3}{20}$ of 180 km   **l** $\frac{17}{20}$ of £140

3 There are 48 computers in an office. $\frac{5}{8}$ of the computers are laptops. Work out the number of laptops in the office.

4 There are 33 students in a class. $\frac{6}{11}$ of the students are boys. How many students in the class are girls?

5 $\frac{5}{6}$ of the distance between 2 towns can be driven on the motorway. The distance between the 2 towns is 180 km. How far can be driven on the motorway?

6 There are 240 students in a year group. $\frac{7}{12}$ of the students are boys. How many students are boys?

Exercise 13B

Give your answer to each question as a fraction in its simplest form.

1 Express the first number as a fraction of the second number.

a 5 and 10	**b** 2 and 12
c 15 and 20	**d** 24 and 32
e 24 and 36	

2 Express the first amount as a fraction of the second amount.

a £30 and £60

b 16 km and 32 km

c 80p and £2

d 8 hours and 1 day

e 40 seconds and 2 minutes

f 20 minutes and $\frac{1}{2}$ hour

g 48 minutes and 1 hour

3 Leon earns £30. He gives £10 to his mother. Write £10 as a fraction of £30

4 Jason spends 3 hours doing homework at the weekend. He spends 90 minutes doing mathematics homework. Write 90 minutes as a fraction of 3 hours.

5 Nicky gets £40 for a present. She spends £32 on some jewellery. Write £32 as a fraction of £40

6 A birthday card cost £1.40. It cost 28p to post. Write 28p as a fraction of £1.40

7 Kimberley travels on a journey lasting 3 hours 20 minutes. She is asleep for 1 hour of the journey. Write 1 hour as a fraction of 3 hours 20 minutes.

8 The cost of a bottle of soft drink increased from £1.20 by 8 pence. Write 8 pence as a fraction of £1.20

Exercise 13C

1 Change these mixed numbers to improper fractions

  a $1\frac{1}{4}$ **b** $2\frac{1}{4}$ **c** $1\frac{2}{3}$ **d** $2\frac{1}{2}$

  e $3\frac{3}{4}$ **f** $4\frac{2}{3}$ **g** $4\frac{1}{5}$ **h** $3\frac{4}{9}$

2 Change these improper fractions to mixed numbers.

  a $\frac{7}{4}$ **b** $\frac{8}{5}$ **c** $\frac{9}{7}$ **d** $\frac{17}{12}$

  e $\frac{19}{4}$ **f** $\frac{13}{5}$ **g** $\frac{17}{6}$ **h** $\frac{11}{3}$

Exercise 13D

Give each answer in its simplest form.

1 Work out

  a $\frac{1}{5}+\frac{2}{5}$ **b** $\frac{1}{9}+\frac{4}{9}$ **c** $\frac{2}{7}+\frac{3}{7}$

  d $\frac{1}{8}+\frac{5}{8}$ **e** $\frac{3}{10}+\frac{3}{10}$ **f** $\frac{5}{12}+\frac{7}{12}$

  g $\frac{4}{5}-\frac{2}{5}$ **h** $\frac{5}{6}-\frac{1}{6}$ **i** $\frac{7}{10}-\frac{3}{10}$

  j $\frac{11}{15}-\frac{2}{15}$

2 Work out

  a $\frac{1}{6}+\frac{2}{5}$ **b** $\frac{3}{8}+\frac{1}{2}$ **c** $\frac{1}{5}+\frac{7}{10}$

  d $\frac{2}{3}+\frac{1}{6}$ **e** $\frac{4}{9}+\frac{1}{6}$ **f** $\frac{5}{6}-\frac{2}{3}$

  g $\frac{7}{8}-\frac{1}{2}$ **h** $\frac{3}{4}-\frac{2}{3}$ **i** $\frac{9}{10}-\frac{2}{5}$

  j $\frac{5}{6}-\frac{1}{2}$

3 Mijan spends $\frac{1}{3}$ of his money on clothes and $\frac{1}{4}$ of his money on football. What fraction of his money does he have left?

4 Last season, Edexcel Town won $\frac{2}{3}$ of its games, drew $\frac{1}{5}$ and lost the rest. What fraction of its matches did it lose?

Exercise 13E

Work out each answer as a mixed number or a fraction in its simplest form

1 a $1\frac{1}{4}+\frac{1}{2}$ **b** $2\frac{1}{3}+\frac{1}{2}$ **c** $\frac{1}{4}+2\frac{1}{3}$

  d $\frac{1}{5}+3\frac{1}{2}$ **e** $1\frac{1}{4}+2\frac{1}{4}$ **f** $3\frac{1}{3}+2\frac{2}{3}$

  g $2\frac{1}{4}+2\frac{1}{2}$ **h** $1\frac{1}{4}+2\frac{1}{3}$ **i** $4\frac{1}{2}+2\frac{2}{3}$

  j $5\frac{2}{3}+2\frac{5}{12}$

2 a $1\frac{1}{2}-\frac{1}{4}$ **b** $2\frac{3}{4}-\frac{1}{2}$ **c** $4\frac{1}{2}-\frac{1}{3}$

  d $2\frac{1}{2}-\frac{3}{8}$ **e** $3\frac{5}{8}-1\frac{1}{4}$ **f** $3\frac{3}{4}-2\frac{2}{3}$

  g $2\frac{1}{4}-1\frac{1}{2}$ **h** $4\frac{3}{8}-2\frac{1}{2}$ **i** $5\frac{1}{4}-3\frac{1}{3}$

  j $6\frac{3}{4}-1\frac{11}{12}$

3 Ben goes on a journey. He takes $2\frac{1}{2}$ hours on the first part and then $1\frac{3}{4}$ hours on the last part. Work out the total time of the journey.

4 Two iron bars are $23\frac{1}{2}$ cm and $21\frac{1}{4}$ cm long. Work out the difference between the lengths of the iron bars.

Exercise 13F

Give each answer in its simplest form.

1 a $3\times\frac{1}{5}$ **b** $2\times\frac{2}{7}$ **c** $4\times\frac{2}{9}$

  d $6\times\frac{1}{12}$ **e** $8\times\frac{1}{10}$ **f** $\frac{1}{6}\times2$

  g $\frac{2}{5}\times2$ **h** $\frac{1}{6}\times4$ **i** $\frac{1}{8}\times6$

  j $\frac{1}{12}\times9$

2 Kerry's cat eats $\frac{2}{3}$ of a tin of cat food every day. How many tins of cat food does Kerry's cat eat in a week?

3 The Houston family drink $\frac{3}{4}$ of a bottle of fruit juice each day for 5 weekdays. How much fruit juice do they drink in total for the 5 weekdays?

Exercise 13G

Give each answer in its simplest form.

1 a $\frac{1}{6}\div2$ **b** $\frac{1}{10}\div2$ **c** $\frac{1}{8}\div3$

  d $\frac{2}{5}\div2$ **e** $\frac{6}{7}\div3$

2 a $\frac{5}{6} \div 3$ **b** $\frac{3}{4} \div 5$ **c** $\frac{5}{8} \div 10$

   d $\frac{9}{20} \div 12$ **e** $\frac{8}{15} \div 12$

3 Share $\frac{1}{2}$ into 3 equal parts.

4 Asif has a chocolate bar.
He eats $\frac{2}{3}$ of the chocolate bar and then
shares the rest equally between two friends.
What fraction of the chocolate bar does
each friend get?

Exercise 13H

Work out and simplify

1 a $\frac{1}{3} \times \frac{4}{5}$ **b** $\frac{1}{4} \times \frac{3}{5}$ **c** $\frac{1}{2} \times \frac{5}{6}$

   d $\frac{1}{5} \times \frac{2}{5}$ **e** $\frac{1}{6} \times \frac{5}{7}$ **f** $\frac{1}{3} \times \frac{1}{10}$

   g $\frac{1}{4} \times \frac{7}{8}$ **h** $\frac{4}{5} \times \frac{1}{4}$ **i** $\frac{5}{6} \times \frac{1}{10}$

2 a $\frac{1}{3}$ of $\frac{3}{4}$ **b** $\frac{1}{2}$ of $\frac{4}{5}$ **c** $\frac{1}{4}$ of $\frac{6}{7}$

   d $\frac{1}{5}$ of $\frac{10}{11}$ **e** $\frac{1}{6}$ of $\frac{9}{10}$

3 In a bag of sweets, two thirds are fruit drops.
One quarter of the fruit drops are
blackcurrant flavoured.
What fraction of sweets in the bag are
blackcurrant flavoured fruit drops?

4 In Bill's CD collection, $\frac{3}{4}$ of the CDs are jazz.
$\frac{1}{3}$ of the jazz CDs are piano.
What fraction of Bill's CD collection are jazz
piano?

Exercise 13I

Work out the following. Give each answer in its
simplest form.

1 a $\frac{2}{3} \times \frac{4}{7}$ **b** $\frac{2}{5} \times \frac{3}{5}$ **c** $\frac{3}{4} \times \frac{5}{8}$

   d $\frac{4}{5} \times \frac{2}{7}$ **e** $\frac{2}{3} \times \frac{3}{7}$ **f** $\frac{3}{4} \times \frac{3}{5}$

   g $\frac{3}{5} \times \frac{10}{11}$ **h** $\frac{3}{4} \times \frac{8}{9}$ **i** $\frac{5}{6} \times \frac{9}{20}$

   j $\frac{5}{8} \times \frac{24}{25}$

2 a $\frac{4}{5}$ of $\frac{5}{12}$ **b** $\frac{3}{8}$ of $\frac{16}{21}$ **c** $\frac{4}{9}$ of $\frac{27}{28}$

   d $\frac{7}{8}$ of $\frac{16}{35}$ **e** $\frac{5}{8}$ of $\frac{24}{35}$

3 $\frac{4}{5}$ of a shape is shaded. $\frac{2}{3}$ of the shaded part is
shaded red. What fraction of the whole
shape is shaded red?

4 John spends $\frac{3}{4}$ of his spare time playing
musical instruments. Of the time spent
playing musical instruments, $\frac{2}{3}$ is spent on
the piano. What fraction of John's spare time
is spent playing the piano?

5 Work out

   a $1\frac{1}{4} \times \frac{1}{5}$ **b** $2\frac{2}{3} \times \frac{5}{8}$ **c** $1\frac{1}{3} \times 1\frac{1}{5}$

   d $2\frac{1}{4} \times 1\frac{1}{3}$ **e** $3\frac{3}{4} \times 2\frac{4}{5}$

Exercise 13J

Give each answer in its simplest form

1 a $\frac{3}{14} \times \frac{7}{9}$ **b** $\frac{8}{9} \times \frac{27}{32}$ **c** $\frac{15}{16} \times \frac{12}{25}$

   d $\frac{13}{15} \times \frac{10}{39}$ **e** $\frac{11}{13} \times \frac{26}{55}$ **f** $\frac{3}{4} \times \frac{7}{9} \times \frac{4}{21}$

2 a $\frac{1}{2} \div \frac{1}{4}$ **b** $\frac{1}{6} \div \frac{1}{2}$ **c** $\frac{3}{5} \div \frac{9}{10}$

   d $\frac{7}{8} \div \frac{3}{4}$ **e** $\frac{5}{9} \div \frac{5}{6}$ **f** $\frac{9}{10} \div \frac{3}{20}$

3 a $2\frac{1}{2} \div \frac{1}{4}$ **b** $1\frac{1}{3} \div \frac{3}{4}$ **c** $2\frac{2}{3} \div 1\frac{1}{9}$

   d $3\frac{3}{4} \div 1\frac{3}{4}$ **e** $1\frac{1}{4} \div 1\frac{3}{4}$ **f** $\frac{8}{9} \div 1\frac{2}{3}$

   g $2\frac{1}{3} \div 1\frac{3}{4}$ **h** $4\frac{4}{5} \div 2\frac{1}{10}$

4 A rectangle carpet is $3\frac{3}{4}$ metres wide and
$4\frac{2}{5}$ metres long. Work out the area of the
carpet.

Chapter 14
Processing, representing and interpreting data

Exercise 14A

1 Here is a pictogram showing the number of
people who played at the local tennis club
on five days last week.

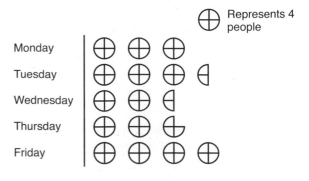

Represents 4 people

Monday	
Tuesday	
Wednesday	
Thursday	
Friday	

a On which day did the greatest number of people play tennis?

b On which day did the least number of people play tennis?

c Write down the number of people who played tennis on
  i Monday
  ii Tuesday.

d Work out the total number of people that played tennis from Monday to Friday.

2 Here is a pictogram. It shows the number of boxes of chocolates sold last week from Monday to Friday.

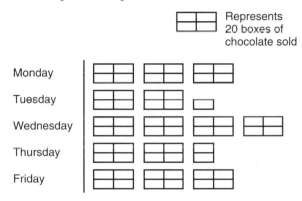

| | Represents 20 boxes of chocolate sold |

a Write down the number of boxes of chocolates sold on
  i Wednesday
  ii Thursday.

b On which day of the week were 45 boxes of chocolates sold?

c On which two days of the week did the shop sell the same number of boxes of chocolates?

3 The table shows the number of hours of sunshine on each of five days.

Draw a pictogram to represent this information.

Use ⊛ to represent 2 hours of sunshine.

Day	Hours of sunshine
Monday	6
Tuesday	11
Wednesday	10
Thursday	12
Friday	7

Exercise 14B

1 Lesley wrote down the colour of each car in the school car park.
The bar chart shows this information.

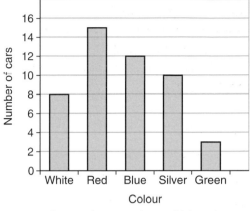

a Write down the number of blue cars.

b What colour were most cars?

c Work out the total number of cars.
(1388 January 2005)

2 The bar chart shows the number of text messages that Sumire sent each day one week.

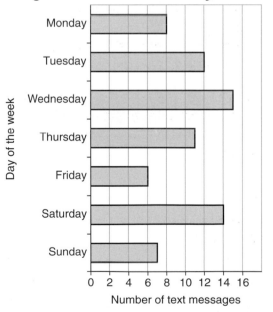

a On which day did Sumire send the greatest number of text messages?

b Write down the number of text messages that she sent on
  i Tuesday   **ii** Thursday.

c On which day did she send 7 text messages?

d Work out the total number of text messages she sent during the week.

3 Fred asked some of his friends which sport they preferred.
The table shows the results.

Sport	Number of friends
Football	20
Running	5
Hockey	12
Rugby	14

Draw a bar chart to represent this information.

4 Six students each sat a maths and a science test. The dual bar chart shows their results.

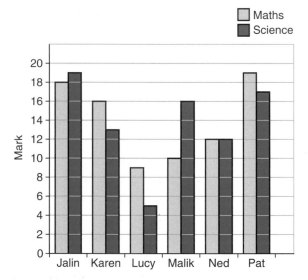

☐ Maths
■ Science

a How many marks did Karen get in her science test?

b How many marks did Malik get in his maths test?

c Which student scored the same number of marks in both tests?

d Two students got a higher mark in the science test than in the maths test.
Write down the names of these two students.

5 The table shows the number of points gained by two girls during 5 games of cards.

	Game 1	Game 2	Game 3	Game 4	Game 5
Laura	5	10	12	7	6
Hannah	8	7	11	9	6

a Draw a dual bar chart to show this information.

b Which girl scored the greatest number of points?

Exercise 14C

1 The table shows information about the colour of 36 horses at a stable.

Colour of horse	Bay	Chestnut	Grey	Black
Frequency	14	10	7	5

a Work out the sector angle for each colour.

b Draw an accurate pie chart to show this information.

2 Sarah asked 40 friends to name their favourite pasta dish. The table shows her results.

Pasta dish	Macaroni Cheese	Lasagne	Spaghetti Bolognese
Frequency	7	18	15

a Work out the sector angle for each pasta dish.

b Draw an accurate pie chart to show this information.

3 Emily asked each of 60 people at an airport which country they were travelling to.
The table shows this information.

Country	America	Australia	Japan	Canada	Hong Kong
Frequency	24	9	10	12	5

Draw an accurate pie chart to show this information.

4 The table shows information about the way 720 pupils travel to school.

Method of transport	Train	Bus	Cycle	Walk	Car
Frequency	90	200	148	186	96

Draw an accurate pie chart to show this information.

Exercise 14D

1 There are 40 fruit trees in an orchard. The pie chart shows information about the number of different types of fruit trees in the orchard.

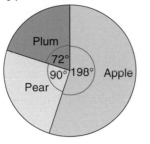

a Which was the most popular type of fruit tree?

b What fraction of the fruit trees were pear trees?

c How many trees were pear trees?

d How many degrees represent one tree on the pie chart?

e How many apple trees were in the orchard?

2 The pie chart gives information about the results of a rugby team's games during one season. The team lost 8 games.

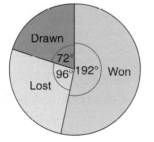

a How many degrees represent one game in the pie chart?

b How many games did the rugby team play during the season?

3 The pie chart shows information about the favourite hot drink of some people.

a What fraction of people preferred hot chocolate? Give your fraction in its simplest form.

5 people said that milk was their favourite hot drink.

b How many degrees represent one person in the pie chart?

c How many people said that
  i coffee   **ii** tea
was their favourite drink?

4 Charlie draws a pie chart to show the number of different makes of car in a car park. He works out these angles for his pie chart.

Type of car	Angle in pie chart
Vauxhall	81°
Ford	93°
Toyota	132°
Rover	48°
Audi	6°

There are 120 cars in the car park.
Work out how many of each make of car is in the car park.

Exercise 14E

1 The line graph shows the number of visitors to a stately home, correct to the nearest hundred, each month for six months.

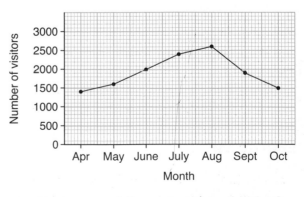

a How many visitors were there in May?

b In which month were there 1900 visitors?

c Describe what happened to the number of visitors between April and August.

2 The table shows the maximum monthly temperatures, in °C, in New York.

Jan	Feb	Mar	Apr	May	Jun	Jul	Aug	Sep	Oct	Nov	Dec
3	3	7	14	20	25	28	27	26	21	11	5

Draw a line graph to show this information.

3 The graph shows the number of DVDs sold each month for 6 months by two different shops.

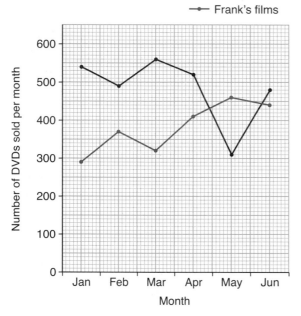

a How many DVDs were sold by Danny's DVDs in March?

b In which month did Frank's films sell 370 DVDs?

c In which month did Frank's films sell more DVDs than Danny's DVDs?

d Describe the sales from January to June at Frank's films.

e Describe the sales from January to June at Danny's DVDs.

Exercise 14F

1 Mr Potts records the number of customers that come into his shop over a period of 30 days.

37 32 48 53 32 47 42 45 33 49
52 32 34 31 38 40 52 36 37 33
34 39 43 52 50 46 44 37 38 32

Number of customers	Tally	Frequency
31–35		
36–40		
41–45		
46–50		
51–55		

a Copy and complete the grouped frequency table.

b Write down the modal class interval.

c Draw a frequency diagram for this information.

2 The histogram shows information about the heights of the girls in a class.

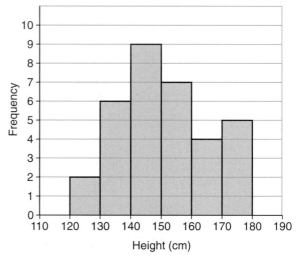

a Write down the modal class interval.

b Work out the total number of girls.

3 The grouped frequency table gives information about the amount of time patients had to wait in a doctor's surgery.

Time (m minutes)	Frequency
$0 \leqslant m < 5$	2
$5 \leqslant m < 10$	5
$10 \leqslant m < 15$	8
$15 \leqslant m < 20$	6
$20 \leqslant m < 25$	3
$25 \leqslant m < 30$	2

a Draw a histogram to show this information.

b Draw a frequency polygon to show this information.

Chapter 15
Graphs 2

Exercise 15A

1 Use a copy of this grid to answer this question

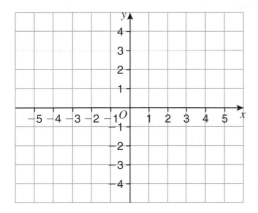

a Write down the equation of the line which passes through the points $(3, 4), (3, 2), (3, -1)$ and $(3, -3)$

b Write down the equation of the line which passes through the points $(-2, 4), (0, 4), (1, 4),$ and $(4, 4),$

c For the rectangle $ABCD$, where the vertices are the points $A(1, 1),$ $B(5, 1), C(5, 3), D(1, 3),$ write down the equation of
  i the horizontal line of symmetry
  ii the vertical line of symmetry.

d For the kite $PQRS$, where the vertices are the points $P(-3, 4), Q(-1, 1),$ $R(-3, -4), S(-5, 1),$ write down the equation of
  i the horizontal diagonal
  ii the vertical diagonal.

2 The point D is $(-5, -8)$.

a Write down the equation of the horizontal line through D.

b Write down the equation of the vertical line through D.

3 Write down the equation of the line through the points

a $(-10, -5)$ and $(-10, 1)$

b $(0, -15)$ and $(-6, -15)$

Exercise 15B

1 a Find the equation of the line which passes through the points $A(4, 6),$ $B(1, 3), C(0, 2), D(-2, 0)$ and $E(-4, -2)$

b Find the equation of the line which passes through the points $V(4, 20),$ $W(3, 15), X(0, 0)$ and $Y(-2, -10)$

2 Here is a table of values for $y = 2x + 2$

x	-2	-1	0	1	2	3
y	-2	0	2	4	6	8

a On a copy of the grid below, draw the graph of $y = 2x + 2$

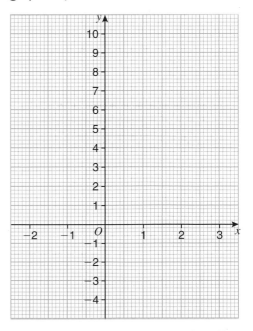

b Write down the coordinates of the point where your graph crosses **i** the y-axis. **ii** the x-axis.

c Use your graph to find the value of x when $y = 5$

3 a Complete this table of values for
$y = 5x - 3$

x	−1	0	1	2	3
y		−3			12

b On a copy of the grid below, draw the graph of $y = 5x - 3$

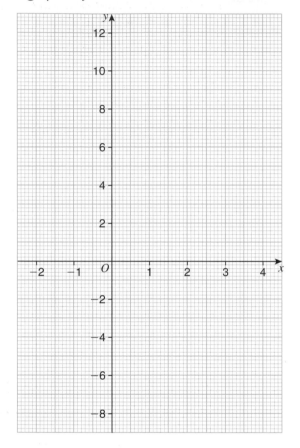

c Use your graph to estimate the value of x when $y = 4$

4 a Copy and complete this table of values for $y = 1 - 2x$

x	−2	−1	0	1	2	3
y	5			−1		

b On a copy of the following grid, draw the graph of $y = 1 - 2x$

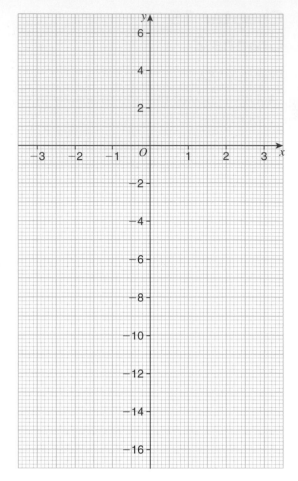

c Write down the coordinates of the point where your graph crosses the y-axis.

d Find an estimate for the coordinates of the point where the graph of $y = x$ crosses the graph of $y = 1 - 2x$

Exercise 15C

1 Find the coordinates of the points where the graphs of the following equations cross the axes.

a $x + y = 1$ **b** $x + y = 4$

c $x + y = 10$ **d** $x + y = 25$

e $x + y = -9$ **f** $x + y = -12$

2 a On the same axes, draw the graphs of
i $x + y = 1$ **ii** $x + y = 4$
iii $x + y = 0$ **iv** $x + y = -2$

b What do you notice about the four graphs you have drawn?

3

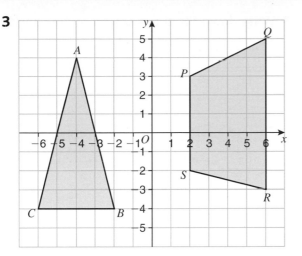

a In triangle ABC find the gradient of the line **i** AB **ii** AC

b In trapezium $PQRS$ find the gradient of the line **i** PQ **ii** RS

4 For each of the lines write down
i the gradient **ii** the y-intercept
a $y = 4x + 5$ **b** $y = x + 2$
c $y = -4x - 2$ **d** $y = 1 - 7x$

Exercise 15D

1 a Copy and complete this table of values for $y = x^2 + 1$

x	−2	−1	0	1	2	3
y	5		1			10

b Draw the graph of $y = x^2 + 1$

c Write down the coordinates of the minimum point.

2 a Copy and complete this table of values for $y = 5 - 2x^2$

x	−3	−2	−1	0	1	2	3
y	−13		3			−3	

b Draw the graph of $y = 5 - 2x^2$

c Write down an estimate for the coordinates of the points where the graph crosses the x-axis.

3 a Complete this table of values for $y = x - x^2$

x	−2	−1	0	1	2	3
y		−2	0		−2	

b Draw the graph of $y = x - x^2$ from $x = -2$ to $x = 3$

c Write down the values of x where the graph crosses the x-axis.

d Write down the equation of the line of symmetry of your graph.

e Use your graph to find an estimate for the maximum value of y.

4 a Complete the table of values for $y = x^2 - 3x + 1$

x	−2	−1	0	1	2	3	4
y	11		1	−1			5

b Draw the graph of $y = x^2 - 3x + 1$ from $x = -2$ to $x = 4$

(1387 June 2006)

Exercise 15E

1 a Draw the graph of $y = x^2 - 4$ from $x = -3$ to $x = 3$

b Use the graph of $y = x^2 - 4$ to find the solutions to the equation $x^2 - 4 = 0$

c **i** On the same axes, draw the graph of $y = 2$

ii Write down the values of the x-coordinates of the points where the two graphs cross.

iii Write down the equation solved by your answers to part **ii**

2 a Draw the graph of $y = x^2 + 2x - 3$ from $x = -4$ to $x = 2$

b Use the graph of $y = x^2 + 2x - 3$ to find the solutions to the equation $x^2 + 2x - 3 = 0$

3 a Draw the graph of $y = 2x^2 - 3x - 2$ from $x = -2$ to $x = 4$

b Use the graph of $y = 2x^2 - 3x - 2$ to find the solutions to the equation $2x^2 - 3x - 2 = 0$

Chapter 16
Measure

Exercise 16A

1 a Write down the number marked with an arrow.

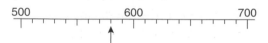

b Write down the number marked with an arrow.

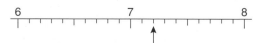

c Copy this number line and find the number 48 on the line.
Mark it with an arrow (↑)

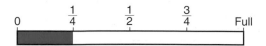

d Copy this number line and find the number 6.7 on the line.
Mark it with an arrow (↑)

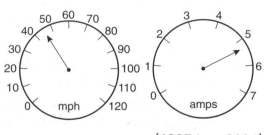

(1387 June 2005)

2 a The diagram shows the scale on a petrol tank.

What fraction of the petrol tank is empty?

b What is the reading on each of these scales?

(1387 June 2004)

3 Write down the times shown on the clocks.

a   **b**

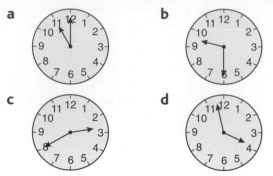

c   **d**

4 Here is a thermometer. The thermometer shows Nazia's temperature, in °C.

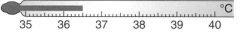

Write down Nazia's temperature.

5 a Write down the number marked with an arrow.

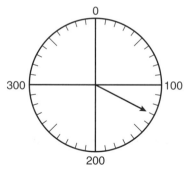

b Write down the number marked with an arrow.

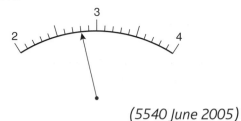

(5540 June 2005)

Exercise 16B

1 Change these times from 12-hour clock times to 24-hour clock times.

a	6 am	**b**	6 pm
c	10 05 am	**d**	10 05 pm
e	2 48 am	**f**	12 30 pm
g	12 30 am	**h**	5 18 pm

2 Change these times from 24-hour clock times to 12-hour clock times, using am or pm

   a 08 00   **b** 03 15

   c 19 55   **d** 10 20

   e 23 58   **f** 12 38

   g 00 18   **h** 20 00

3 Write each of these times in
     i the 12-hour clock
     ii the 24-hour clock.

   a half past nine in the morning

   b ten to eleven at night

   c quarter past 12 in the afternoon

   d twenty past 7 in the evening

   e noon

   f forty minutes after midnight

Exercise 16C

1 a Change these times to minutes.
     i 5 hours
     ii 20 hours
     iii 3 hours 20 minutes
     iv $4\frac{1}{4}$ hours
     v 420 seconds

   b Change these times to hours.
     i 6 days
     ii 2 weeks
     iii 180 minutes
     iv 540 minutes
     v $3\frac{1}{2}$ days

2 Change these times to minutes and seconds.

   a 130 seconds

   b 640 seconds

   c 1245 seconds

3 Change these times to hours and minutes.

   a 550 minutes

   b 158 minutes

   c 923 minutes

4 Taking a year as 365 days, how many seconds are there in a year?

5 Here are the times on five clocks.

02:53	01:56	03:20	02:59	03:02
A	B	C	D	E

   a Write down the letter of the clock that shows a time nearest to 03 : 00

   b Work out the difference, in minutes, between the time shown on clock **A** and the time shown on clock **E**.
                  (1388 November 2005)

6 Yesterday Debbie worked for 4 hours 30 minutes before lunch. After lunch yesterday, she worked for another 2 hours 40 minutes. Work out the total time, in hours and minutes, that Debbie worked yesterday.

7 In a factory the night shift starts at 22 30 and finishes at 08 15. Work out the length of the night shift. Give your answer in hours and minutes.
                  (4400 May 2005)

8 Here is part of a railway timetable.

Manchester	07 53	09 17	10 35	11 17	13 30	14 36	16 26
Stockport	08 01	09 26	10 43	11 25	13 38	14 46	16 39
Macclesfield	08 23	09 38	10 58	11 38	13 52	14 58	17 03
Congleton	08 31	–	–	11 49	–	15 07	17 10
Kidsgrove	08 37	–	–	–	–	–	17 16
Stoke-on-Trent	08 49	10 00	11 23	12 03	14 12	15 19	17 33

A train leaves Manchester at 10 35

   a At what time should this train arrive in Stoke-on-Trent?

Doris has to go to a meeting in Stoke-on-Trent. She will catch the train in Stockport. She needs to arrive in Stoke-on-Trent before 2 pm for her meeting.

   b Write down the time of the latest train she can catch in Stockport.

   c Work out how many minutes it should take the 14 36 train from Manchester to get to Stoke-on-Trent.

The 14 36 train from Manchester to Stoke-on-Trent takes less time than the 16 26 train from Manchester to Stoke-on-Trent.

d How many minutes less?

(1387 June 2004)

Exercise 16D

1 Copy and complete this table.
Write a sensible unit for each measurement.

Measurement	Metric	Imperial
The height of a door	....	feet
The distance between two towns	kilometres	....

(1388 April 2005)

2 Use metric units to write down an estimate for

a the height of a man

b the weight of a calculator.

(4400 November 2005)

3 The picture shows a man standing next to a giraffe.

The man and the giraffe are drawn to the same scale.

a Write down an estimate for the height, in metres, of the man.

b Estimate the height, in metres, of this giraffe.

(1387 June 2005)

4 Copy and complete this table by writing a sensible unit for each measurement.

Measurement	Metric unit	Imperial unit
The length of your hand	centimetres	....
The weight of a dog	....	pounds
The volume of petrol in a car's petrol tank	....	gallons

5 Copy and complete the following sentences by writing a sensible metric unit on the dotted line.

i There are 330 .... of cola in a can.

ii A television set weighs 21 ....

iii A brick is 215 .... long.

iv There are 425 .... of baked beans in a tin. *(1385 June 2002)*

6 Write down the name of the **metric** unit which is usually used to measure the weight of a person. *(1388 April 2006)*

7 Copy and complete the table by writing a sensible metric unit on each dotted line. The first one has been done for you.

The distance from London to Birmingham	179 kilometres
The weight of a twenty pence coin	5
The height of the tallest living man	232
The volume of lemonade in a glass	250

(1387 June 2005)

Exercise 16E

1 Change these lengths to centimetres.

a 3 m   **b** 24 mm   **c** 0.81 m

d 4 km   **e** 87.3 mm   **f** 6.9 m

g 0.072 km

2 Change these lengths to metres.

a 9 km   **b** 200 cm   **c** 7300 mm

d 835 cm   **e** 2.73 km

3 Change these weights to kilograms.

   a 9000g   **b** 500 g   **c** 6200 g

   d 7 tonnes   **e** 0.3 tonnes

4 Change these weights to grams.

   a 3 kg   **b** 2.2 kg   **c** 5000 mg

   d 0.67 kg   **e** 843 mg

5 Paula ran in the 10 000 metres race in the Olympic Games.
Change 10 000 metres to kilometres.

6 a   Change 8 kilometres to metres.

                             (5540 June 2005)

   b **i** Change 5.6 metres to centimetres.

        ii Change 6700 millilitres to litres.

                            (1388 April 2006)

   c Change 5000 metres to kilometres.

                            (1387 June 2005)

   d Change 5.7 kg to grams.

                            (1388 April 2005)

   e Write 30 cm in metres.

Exercise 16F

1 The chart shows the shortest distances, in kilometres, between pairs of cities.
For example, the shortest distance between London and Manchester is 300 km.

London				
196	Nottingham			
300	101	Manchester		
325	158	56	Liverpool	
639	446	346	348	Glasgow

   a Write down the shortest distance between Nottingham and Liverpool.

Daniel drives from London to Manchester by the shortest route. He has driven 137 km.

   b Work out how many more kilometres he must drive.

   c Write down the names of the two cities which are the least distance apart.

                            (1388 January 2003)

2 Linda drove from Liverpool to Glasgow by the shortest route. She drove at an average speed of 60 km/h. Using the chart in question **1**, work out the time, in hours, that her journey took.

3 The diagram shows the distances, in miles, between some service areas on the M1 motorway.

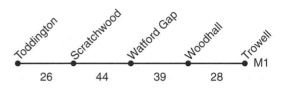

For example, the distance between Toddington and Watford Gap is 70 miles.

   a Copy and complete the table.

Toddington				
26	Scratchwood			
70		Watford Gap		
	83	39	Woodhall	
	111		28	Trowell

                            (1388 January 2004)

Sunil drove from Toddington to Watford Gap in $1\frac{1}{4}$ hours.

   b Work out Sunil's average speed in mph.

4 A car has an average speed of 60 km/h.
It travels for a time of 4 hours.
Work out the distance the car travels.

5 Mary drove from her home to her friend's house. The distance she drove was $31\frac{1}{2}$ km.
She left home at 10 40 am and arrived at her friend's house at 11 15 am. Work out Mary's average speed for her journey.
Give your answer in km/h.

6 Ann drove from Glasgow to Poole, a distance of 210 km.
The journey took 2 hours 40 minutes.
Work out Ann's average speed.

                            (1387 November 2005)

7 Fred runs 200 metres in 21.2 seconds.
Work out Fred's average speed.
Give your answer in metres per second
correct to one decimal place.
(1387 November 2004)

8 A train travels at a speed of 180 kilometres
per hour.
Graham said that 180 kilometres per hour is
the same as 50 metres per second.
Show working to show that Graham is correct.
(5540 June 2004)

9 Niall went on a cycle ride. For the first part of
the ride, he cycled 40 km at an average speed
of 16 km/h. For the rest of his ride, he cycled
for 2 hours at an average speed of 12 km/h.

  a Work out the total distance Niall cycled.

  b Work out the total time taken by Niall
  on his ride.

  c Work out Niall's average speed for the
  whole ride. Give your answer in km/h,
  correct to one decimal place.

Exercise 16G

1 A piece of silver has a mass of 52.5 grams
and a volume of 5 cm³.
Work out the density of the silver.

2 A cylinder has a volume of 2260 cm³.
The cylinder is made of material that has a
density of 1.5 g/cm³.
Work out the mass of the cylinder.
(1388 April 2005)

3 Aluminium has a density of 2700kg/m³.
Work out the volume of a piece of
aluminium with a mass of 8100 kg.

4 A block of wood has a volume of 140 cm³.
The wood has a density of 1.2 grams per cm³.
Work out the mass of the block of wood.
(1388 April 2005)

5 A copper rod has a mass of 427.2 grams and
a volume of 48 cm³.

  a Work out the density of copper.

  Another copper rod has a mass of 1.78 kg.

  b Work out the volume of this copper rod.

Chapter 17 Percentages

Exercise 17A

1 Write each percentage as a fraction.

  a 67%   **b** 3%   **c** 39%

  d 13%   **e** 89%   **f** 51%

2 Write each percentage as a fraction in its
simplest form.

  a 6%   **b** 60%   **c** 35%

  d 24%   **e** 88%   **f** 55%

3 Write each percentage as a decimal.

  a 46%   **b** 71%   **c** 5%

  d 30%   **e** 14.5%   **f** 3.2%

4 18% of children go by train to school.
What fraction of children go by train to
school.
Give your fraction in its simplest form.

5 95% of households own a television.
Write down the fraction of households that
does **not** own a television.
Give your fraction in its simplest form

6 What percentage of each of the following
shapes is shaded?

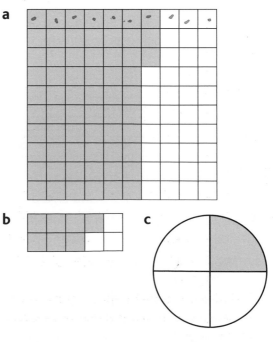

7 Write each percentage as
  i a fraction in its simplest form **ii** a decimal.
  a $37\frac{1}{2}\%$ **b** $5\frac{1}{2}\%$ **c** $7\frac{1}{4}\%$

Exercise 17B

1 a Write 28% as a decimal.
  b Write $\frac{1}{4}$ as a decimal.
  c Which is bigger 28% or $\frac{1}{4}$?

2 a Write $\frac{7}{10}$ as a decimal.
  b Write 71% as a decimal.
  c Which is bigger $\frac{7}{10}$ or 71%?

3 In each part, write the numbers in order of size. Start with the smallest number.
  a 0.52 $\frac{1}{2}$ 49% **b** $\frac{9}{10}$ 85% 0.89

4 a Write $\frac{11}{40}$ as a decimal.
  b Write 27% as a decimal.
  c Which is bigger $\frac{11}{40}$ or 27%?

5 Write these numbers in order of size. Start with the smallest number.
  a 0.55 $\frac{8}{15}$ 53% $\frac{4}{7}$ **b** 0.07 $\frac{1}{20}$ 6% $\frac{3}{40}$
  c 0.4 $\frac{7}{15}$ 36% $\frac{3}{7}$ **d** 63% 0.6 $\frac{2}{3}$ 66%

Exercise 17C

1 Work out
  a 50% of 40 **b** 25% of 20
  c 10% of 80 **d** 50% of 24
  e 20% of 50 **f** 25% of 48
  g 75% of 16 **h** 75% of 80

2 Work out
  a 10% of £400 **b** 50% of £280
  c 25% of 40 g **d** 75% of 200 m
  e 2% of £300 **f** 45% of 400 kg
  g 12% of $200 **h** 5% of £420

3 Mikhail invests £400. The interest rate is 4% per year. How much interest will he receive after one year?

4 There are 600 students at Northolt School. 55% of these 600 students are girls. How many of the students are girls?

5 Work out 70% of £340
  (1388 November 2005)

6 Work out
  a 24% of £30 **b** 5% of 45.6 m
  c 80% of 65 kg **d** 6.5% of £300
  e 4.2% of £2500 **f** $17\frac{1}{2}\%$ of £560
  g $2\frac{1}{4}\%$ of 30 m

7 Alex invests £6200. The interest rate is 4.1% per year. How much interest will he receive at the end of 1 year?

8 Bhavana did a maths test. There was a total of 60 marks for the test. Bhavana got 45% of the marks. Work out how many marks she got.

9 The price of a television is £385. Jim pays a deposit of 15% of the price. Work out how much he pays.

10 Ezra earns £325 per week. He spends 42% of his weekly wage on rent. Work out how much Ezra spends on rent.

11 There are 24 600 books in a library. 46% of the books in the library are fiction. Work out how many fiction books there are in the library.

12 62% of the workers in a factory are female. There are 850 workers at the factory. Work out how many of the workers are female.

Exercise 17D

1 Janet earns £400 per week. She gets a wage rise of 10%. How much does Janet earn per week after her rise?

2 In a sale, prices are reduced by 15%. Work out the sale price of a washing machine that normally costs £360

3 Alan puts £800 into a bank account. At the end of one year 4% interest is added. How much is in his account at the end of one year?

4 Prandeep buys a car for £7800. The value of the car depreciates by 30% each year. Work out the value of the car at the end of one year.

5 A holiday normally costs £780 It is reduced by 17.5%. How much will the holiday now cost?

6 William's salary is £24 000 His salary increases by 4%. Work out William's new salary.
(1388 March 2005)

7 The price of a DVD player was £120 In a sale, the price is reduced by 35%. Work out the sale price of the DVD player.
(1388 November 2005)

8 Alistair sells books. He sells each book for £7.60 plus VAT at $17\frac{1}{2}$%. He sells 1650 books. Work out how much money Alistair receives.
(1387 June 2005)

9 Kunal bought a bag of oranges for £5. He sold the bag of oranges. He made a profit of 20%. Work out how much he sold the bag of oranges for.
(1388 April 2006)

Exercise 17E

1 Write as a percentage
  a £5 out of £20
  b 3 m out of 6 m
  c 6 cm out of 60 cm
  d 80 kg out of 100 kg
  e $40 out of $200
  f 21 g out of 28 g

2 Write as a percentage
  a 50p out of £2
  b 80 cm out of 4 m
  c 300 m out of 1 km
  d 24 minutes out of 1 hour
  e 45 mm out of 6 cm
  f 80p out of £4

3 Linda's mark in a maths test was 36 out of 50 Find 36 out of 50 as a percentage.
(1388 January 2005)

4 Lesley's mark in a geography test was 48 out of 60 Work out 48 out of 60 as a percentage.
(1388 March 2002)

5 In a survey, 64 out of 80 children said they like fish fingers.
  a What percentage of the children like fish fingers?
  b What percentage of the children do **not** like fish fingers?

6 Frank buys a crate of 60 apples. He finds that 9 of the apples are rotten.
  a What percentage of the apples are rotten?
  b What percentage of the apples are **not** rotten?

7 Jalin was given £600. He put £420 out of the £600 into a savings account. What percentage of the £600 did Jalin put into a savings account?

Chapter 18
Averages and range

Exercise 18A

1 Here is a list of five numbers
  5   7   9   4   5
  a Write down the mode.
  b Find the median.
  c Find the range.
  d Work out the mean.

2 The list shows the shoe sizes of ten men.

9   11   10   9   10   8   12   7   10   9

a   Write down the mode.

b   Find the range.

c   Find the median.

d   Work out the mean shoe size.

3 Here are the marks of eight students in a test.

43   35   67   56   76   48   29   81

a   Work out the range of these marks.

b   Work out the mean mark.

4 Here are the number of children in 5 families.

3   1   4   3   2

a   Work out the mean number of children per family.

b   The mean number of children of another 5 families is 1.8. Work out the total number of children in these 5 families.

c   Find the mean number of children of all ten families.

5 Daniel plays a computer game.
Here are his scores in six games.

260   245   375   275   195   240

a   Find his median score.

b   Find the range of his scores.

c   Work out his mean score.

d   Daniel plays another game. His mean score is now 300. Work out Daniel's score in this game.

Exercise 18B

1 The table shows the ages of 10 children in a play group.

Ages (in years)	Number of children
2	1
3	6
4	3

a   Write down the modal age.

b   Find the range of the ages.

c   Find the median age.

d   Work out the mean age.

2 The table shows the numbers of passengers in each of 20 taxis arriving at a railway station.

Number of passengers	Frequency
0	3
1	2
2	3
3	5
4	6
5	1

a   Work out the total number of passengers in these 20 taxis.

b   Work out the median number of passengers.

c   Work out the mean number of passengers per taxi.

3 The table gives information about the number of letters received by Mr Lake in the last 20 days.

Number of letters	Frequency
0	3
1	4
2	5
3	8

a   Work out the number of letters that Mr Lake received in the last 20 days.

b   Find the median number of letters received.

c   Work out the mean number of letters received.

Exercise 18C

1 The stem and leaf diagram shows the number of spelling mistakes made by each student in a class in an essay.

```
0 | 7 9
1 | 1 2 2 3 5 8 8
2 | 0 1 3 5 5 5 7 8 9 9
3 | 0 0 3 5 6
```

KEY
2 | 3   stands for 23 mistakes

a   Find the number of students in the class.

b Write down how many students made more than 25 spelling mistakes.

c Write down how many students made less than 16 spelling mistakes.

d Find the range of the number of spelling mistakes.

e Find the median number of spelling mistakes.

2 The table gives the mean number of children per family in each of 20 countries.

2.3	3.4	3.6	4.3	3.2
4.1	2.8	3.7	1.9	2.2
2.3	2.5	1.8	2.3	2.2
2.7	2.0	1.9	1.7	3.0

a Draw a stem and leaf diagram to show this information.

b Use your stem and leaf diagram to find
i the range   **ii** the median.

Exercise 18D

1

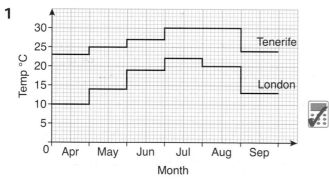

The diagram shows the average midday temperature in London and in Tenerife during the summer months.

a In which months is the average midday temperature normally the highest in Tenerife?

b During which month is there the greatest difference between the average midday temperature between London and Tenerife?

c Write down the average midday temperature for London in May.

d Work out the mean average midday temperature for June to August in Tenerife.

(1385 June 1998)

2 The back to back stem and leaf diagram shows the weight, in kg, of each of 30 boys and 30 girls in a survey.

Girls		Boys
9 8 4 3 3 1	**4**	7 8 8
9 8 7 6 6 4 3 2 2 1 1 1 5	**5**	2 5 6 7 8
9 8 7 4 3 2 2 0 6	**6**	0 1 3 4 4 5 6 8 9 9 9
5 2 2 1 7	**7**	1 1 3 5 7 8 9
	8	0 1 1 3

KEY
6 | 9 means 69 kg

a Find the range of the weights for
i the boys   **ii** the girls.

b Find the median of the weights for
i the boys   **ii** the girls.

c Compare and comment on the weights of the boys and girls.

Exercise 18E

1 Twenty people took part in a doughnut eating competition. The number of doughnuts eaten by each person, in a 10-minute period, is shown in the table

Doughnuts eaten	Number of people
1 to 5	0
6 to 10	1
11 to 15	4
16 to 20	6
21 to 25	8
26 to 30	1

a Find the class interval which contains the median.

b Work out an estimate for the mean number of doughnuts eaten.

2 The table gives information about the time taken by 20 students to travel to school.

Time (t minutes)	Frequency
$0 < t \leqslant 5$	2
$5 < t \leqslant 10$	8
$10 < t \leqslant 15$	4
$15 < t \leqslant 20$	3
$20 < t \leqslant 25$	3

Work out an estimate for the mean time.

(1388 March 2006)

3 The table shows information about the number of words in each sentence of an article in a newspaper.

Number of words	Frequency
$0 < t \leqslant 5$	2
$5 < t \leqslant 10$	5
$10 < t \leqslant 15$	12
$15 < t \leqslant 20$	13
$20 < t \leqslant 25$	10
$25 < t \leqslant 30$	8

a   Find the class interval which contains the median.

b   Work out an estimate for the mean number of words in each sentence.

Chapter 19
Equations and inequalities

Exercise 19A

1 Solve these equations.

a $x + 3 = 7$
b $y - 1 = 2$
c $5 + z = 11$
d $9 - a = 2$
e $b - 7 = 6$
f $2 + c = 7$
g $24 - d - 4$
h $8 = e + 3$
i $0 = 2 - f$
j $18 = 7 + g$

2 Solve these equations.

a $2x = 40$
b $3y = 15$
c $4z = 8$
d $5p = 55$
e $14 = 2q$
f $\dfrac{r}{2} = 3$

g $\dfrac{s}{2} = 6$
h $\dfrac{t}{3} = 10$
i $6 = \dfrac{u}{5}$
j $\dfrac{24}{x} = 8$
k $4 = \dfrac{36}{y}$

Exercise 19B

Use the balance method to solve these equations.

1   $6x = 18$
2   $a - 5 = 21$
3   $4b = 52$
4   $9 = c + 6$
5   $2d + 5 = 13$
6   $3e - 7 = 17$
7   $5f + 10 = 25$
8   $7g - 14 = 21$
9   $9 + 2m = 27$
10   $5 + 2n = 27$
11   $21 = 2p - 9$
12   $4 = 8q + 4$
13   $17 = 3r - 4$
14   $33 = 4s - 15$
15   $12 + 7y - 2 = 52$
16   $\dfrac{x + 2}{2} = 5$
17   $\dfrac{y - 6}{4} = 7$
18   $\dfrac{x}{5} - 2 = 1$
19   $2 = \dfrac{p - 7}{7}$
20   $7 = \dfrac{2q - 3}{3}$

Exercise 19C

Solve these equations.

1   $2x = 1$
2   $2y + 3 = 8$
3   $3a + 5 - 9$
4   $4b + 10 = 13$
5   $5c - 1 = 0$
6   $5d + 3 = 15$
7   $8e + 3 = 10$
8   $6f - 24 = 9$
9   $4g + 6 = 15$
10   $8 + 3h = 15$
11   $5 + 2k = 24$
12   $0 = 8m - 6$
13   $9 = 2n + 6$
14   $9 = 8 + 3p$
15   $-2 + 8x = 11$
16   $2 + 10y - 15 = 3$
17   $\dfrac{2p + 1}{2} = 1$
18   $\dfrac{3x - 2}{2} = 3$
19   $\dfrac{2x}{5} - 2 = 3$
20   $\dfrac{2 + 5y}{3} = 3$

Exercise 19D

Solve

1 $3a = -12$

2 $4b + 27 = 3$

3 $2c + 9 = 4$

4 $9 - 4d = 33$

5 $31 + 4e = 11$

6 $1 = 6f + 4$

7 $3 = 2h + 16$

8 $26 = 32 + 8k$

9 $0 = 15 + 2m$

10 $4n + 2 = -7$

11 $3p - 4 = -13$

12 $2 - 5q = 13$

13 $-3 - 7r = 16$

14 $13 = 20 + 4s$

15 $21 = 8 - 10t$

16 $7 + \dfrac{x}{2} = 3$

17 $\dfrac{3 - y}{3} = 3$

18 $\dfrac{2z + 21}{5} = 2$

Exercise 19E

1 Brendan thinks of a number. He multiplies the number by 6 then adds 17. His answer is 59. Work out the number that Brendan thinks of.

2 Four buses took 200 people from Middleton to Blackpool last Tuesday.
There were x people on each of the first three buses and 20 less people on the fourth bus.

  a Write down an expression, in terms of x, for the number of people on the fourth bus.

  b By forming an equation, work out the value of x.

3 The width of a rectangle is x centimetres.
The length of the rectangle is $(x + 4)$ centimetres.

  a Find an expression, in terms of x, for the perimeter of the rectangle.
Give your expression in its simplest form.

The perimeter of the rectangle is 54 centimetres.

  b Work out the length of the rectangle.

(1388 June 2005)

4

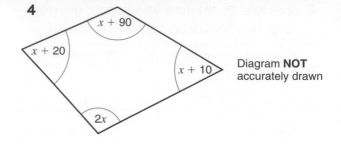

Diagram **NOT** accurately drawn

The sizes of the angles, in degrees, of the quadrilateral are

$$x + 10 \qquad 2x \qquad x + 90 \qquad x + 20$$

a Use this information to write down an equation in terms of x.

b Use your answer to part **a** to work out the size of the smallest angle of the quadrilateral.

(1387 November 2005)

5 The lengths, in centimetres, of the sides of a quadrilateral are

$$2x \qquad x + 6 \qquad 4x - 12 \qquad 30 - 3x$$

a Explain why x must be
  i greater than 3   **ii** less than 10

The perimeter of the quadrilateral is 48 cm.

b Use this information to write down an equation in terms of x.

c Find the value of x.

d The angles of the quadrilateral are not all equal. Explain why the quadrilateral is a rhombus.

Exercise 19F

Solve these equations.

1 $2(x + 3) = 14$

2 $4(y - 2) = 32$

3 $3(z + 3) = 0$

4 $2(a - 1) = 9$

5 $8(b + 2) = 28$

6 $5(2c - 5) = 2$

7 $2(4d + 1) = 14$

8 $2(3e + 7) = 17$

9 $4(2f - 3) = 2$

10 $3(g + 2) = 10$

11 $2(1 - h) = 7$

12 $5(3 - 4m) = 35$

13 $18 = 3(4n + 3)$

14 $26 = 7 + 2(p + 1)$

15 $3(4q + 1) - 7q = 10$

16 $5(x + 5) - x = 21$

17 Solve $5(2y + 3) = 20$
(1387 November 2005)

Exercise 19G

In questions **1–18**, solve the equations.

1 $7x = 5x + 4$

2 $5y = 3y + 6$

3 $3z = z - 16$

4 $3a = 16 - a$

5 $2b = 8 - 3b$

6 $7c = 4 + 2c$

7 $3d + 1 = 2(d + 1)$

8 $2(e + 5) = e + 8$

9 $4(3f - 1) = 2f + 9$

10 $2(5g + 7) = 7g + 11$

11 $2(2h + 1) - 16 - 3h$

12 $5(k - 1) = 3k - 19$

13 $3(2m - 1) = 4(m - 1)$

14 $3(n + 2) = 2(n + 3)$

15 $2(4p - 7) = 2(1 - p)$

16 $x - 2 = \dfrac{x}{2}$

17 $\dfrac{2y}{3} = y - 5$

18 $8 - \dfrac{3x}{5} = x$

19 Solve the equation $5(x - 3) = 2x - 22$
(1388 March 2006)

20

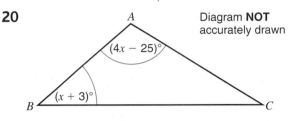

Diagram **NOT** accurately drawn

ABC is a triangle
Angle $A = (4x - 25)°$.
Angle $B = (x + 3)°$.
The size of angle A is **three** times the size of angle B.
Work out the value of x.
(1388 November 2005)

21 Hassan, Joanne and David are selling their cars. Hassan's car has done 2550 miles more than Joanne's car and David's car has done 1500 miles less than Joanne's car. Joanne's car has done x miles.

a Write down an expression, in terms of x, for the number of miles David's car has done.

b Hassan's car has done four times as many miles as David's car. By forming an equation, find the value of x.

c How many miles has Hassan's car done?

Exercise 19H and 19I

1 Copy these statements and state whether each of them is TRUE or FALSE

a $2 > 5$

b $7 < 8$

c $4 \geqslant 4$

d $-4 \leqslant -5$

e $0 - 2 > 1 - 4$

2 Copy and complete by inserting a positive whole number so that the statements are true

   a $5 + \ldots \leqslant 6$

   b $8 - \ldots > 5$

   c $15 - 4 < 8.5 + \ldots$

   d $\ldots - 7 < -5 + 1$

3 Write down the inequality shown on the number line:

a

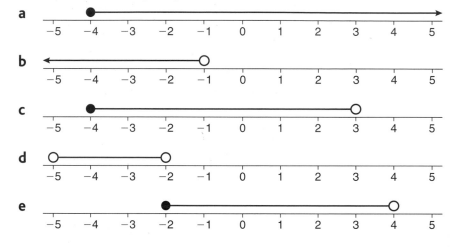

b

c

d

e

4 On a number line, show the inequality

   a $x < -2$ **b** $x \geqslant -1$ **c** $-3 < x < -1$ **d** $0 \leqslant x \leqslant 2$ **e** $-1 \leqslant x < 5$

Exercise 19J

1 Solve these inequalities.

   a $x - 3 < 6$ **b** $x + 1 > 4$

   c $3x \leqslant 18$ **d** $6x \geqslant 9$

   e $2x + 13 > 9$ **f** $3x - 5 < 7$

   g $8x + 15 \leqslant 3$ **h** $10x - 5 \geqslant 0$

   i $8x > 2x + 14$ **j** $7x \geqslant 20 + 3x$

   k $3x \leqslant 4 - 5x$ **l** $5x - 3 \geqslant 9 - 5x$

2 a Solve the inequality
       $8x + 7 \leqslant 16 - 10x$

   b Show your solution on a number line.

Exercise 19K

1 $3 \leqslant x < 6$
   x is an integer.
   Write down all the possible values of x.

2 $-5 \leqslant y \leqslant -3$
   y is an integer.
   Write down all the possible values of y.

3 $-3 \leqslant z < 2$
   z is an integer.
   Write down all the possible values of z.

4 $-4 < 2x \leqslant 6$
   x is an integer.
   Write down all the possible values of x.

5 $-3 < y - 2 < 2$
   y is an integer.
   Write down all the possible values of y.

6 $6a - 3 \leqslant 21$
   a is a **positive** integer.
   Write down all the possible values of a.

7 $3b + 10 > 1$

b is a **negative** integer.

Write down all the possible values of b.

8 a Solve the inequality $7x - 3 > 17$

b x is a whole number such that $7x - 3 > 17$. Write down the smallest value of x.

(1388 November 2005)

Chapter 20
Powers and roots

Exercise 20A

1 Write as powers

  a $7 \times 7 \times 7$

  b $4 \times 4 \times 4 \times 4 \times 4$

  c $2 \times 2 \times 2 \times 2 \times 2 \times 2$

2 Work out

  a 6^2 **b** 3^2

  c 0^2 **d** 2^4

  e $(-10)^3$ **f** 5^3

  g $(-2)^3$ **h** 1^5

  i $(-3)^2$ **j** 100^3

3 Work out

  a $\sqrt{25}$ **b** $\sqrt{36}$

  c $\sqrt{4} \times \sqrt{100}$ **d** $\sqrt{9} \times \sqrt{49}$

  e $\sqrt[3]{27}$ **f** $\sqrt[3]{64}$

  g $\sqrt{15^2}$ **h** $\sqrt{2 \times 8}$

  i $\sqrt{2 \times 18}$ **j** $2^4 - 3^2$

  k $2^4 \times \sqrt{9}$

4 Write down the negative square roots of

  a 36   **b** 4   **c** 64

  d 81   **e** 49

5 Write each of these numbers as products of powers of its prime factors.

  a 24   **b** 40

  c 75   **d** 144

  e 160   **f** 96

  g 112   **h** 500

  i 432   **j** 576

Exercise 20B

1 Work out

  a 3×2^2 **b** $12 \div 2^2$

  c $36 \div 3^2$ **d** $8 - 2^2$

  e 12×2^2 **f** $2^3 \times 3$

  g 9×1^2 **h** $8^2 - 2^2$

2 Work out

  a $5 - 4^2$ **b** $7 - 3^2$

  c $(14 \div 2)^2$ **d** $(15 \div 5)^3$

  e $2^3 - 3^2$ **f** $(9 - 3)^2$

  g $(2 \times 4)^2$ **h** $(8 - 4)^3$

3 Work out

  a $6^2 - 3^2$ **b** $7^2 - 3^2$

  c $3^3 + 3^2 + 3$ **d** $(2 \times 5)^3$

  e $64 \div 4^2$ **f** $6^2 - (3 + 1)^2$

4 Work out

  a $\sqrt{49} \times 2$ **b** $\sqrt{16} \times 4$

  c $2^3 \div \sqrt{16}$ **d** $\sqrt{36} \times 2^3$

  e $\sqrt{25} \times 5$ **f** $3^3 \div \sqrt{9}$

5 Work out

  a $\sqrt{36} \times \sqrt{4}$ **b** $\sqrt{36} + \sqrt{4}$

  c $\sqrt{100} \div \sqrt{4}$ **d** $\sqrt{25} \times \sqrt[3]{1000}$

  e $\sqrt{64} \times \sqrt[3]{64}$ **f** $\sqrt{100} \div \sqrt{16}$

Exercise 20C

1 Write as powers of 2

  a $2^3 \times 2^5$ **b** $2^2 \times 2^7$ **c** $2^4 \times 2^4$

  d $2^5 \times 2^4$ **e** $2^8 \times 2$

2 Write as powers of 5

  a $5^5 \div 5^2$ **b** $5^6 \div 5^4$ **c** $5^8 \div 5^2$

  d $5^7 \div 5^4$ **e** $5^9 \div 5^3$

3 Write as powers of a single number.

a $6^8 \div 6^2$ **b** 100×10^5

c $\dfrac{3^6 \times 3^4}{3^2}$ **d** $\dfrac{5^6 \times 5^8}{5^{10}}$

e $\dfrac{6^8 \times 6^4}{6^5}$ **f** $\dfrac{7^4 \times 7^7}{7^8}$

g $4^8 \times 4^2 \times 4$

4 Work out the value of the following.

a $5^5 \div 5^5$ **b** $6^8 \div 6^6$ **c** $\dfrac{4^2 \times 4^3}{4^4}$

d $\dfrac{3^{10}}{3^6 \times 3^2}$ **e** $\dfrac{2^6 \times 2^4}{2^5}$

5 Find the reciprocals of these numbers.

a $\frac{1}{2}$ **b** 4 **c** $\frac{4}{5}$

d 3 **e** -2

6 Find each value of n.

a $20 = 5 \times 2^n$ **b** $24 = 3 \times 2^n$

c $36 = 3^2 \times 2^n$ **d** $162 = 2 \times 3^n$

e $400 = 5^2 \times 2^n$

7 $108 = 2^m \times 3^n$ where m and n are whole numbers. Find the value of m and the value of n.

8 $250 = 2^m \times 5^n$ where m and n are whole numbers. Find the value of m and the value of n.

9 $504 = 2^m \times 3^n \times 7$ where m and n are whole numbers. Find the value of m and the value of n.

Exercise 20D

1 Work out

a 7.2^2 **b** 16^2 **c** 4.3^2

d 0.52^2 **e** 99^2

2 Work out

a $23 + 13^2$ **b** $640 - 24^2$

c $49^2 + 32^2$ **d** $60^2 - 24^2$

e $3.6^2 - 3.5^2$

3 Work out

a 4.1^3 **b** 11^3

c $21^3 - 20^3$ **d** $1000 - 8^3$

e $16^3 - 14^3$

4 Find the square root of each of these numbers

a 676 **b** 324 **c** 841

d 4096 **e** 5.29

5 Work out each of the following. Give your answers correct to 1 decimal place.

a 6.3^2 **b** $\sqrt{20}$

c $2.5 \times \sqrt{10}$ **d** $3.1^2 + \sqrt{20.5}$

e $\dfrac{1.2^2 + 5.6}{2.7}$ **f** $\sqrt{208} - \sqrt{140}$

g $\dfrac{6.4}{2.8 \times 1.7^2}$ **h** $(\sqrt{6.34})^3$

6 Work out the area of a square which has sides of length 6.3 cm.

7 Work out the area of a square which has a perimeter of length 23.2 cm

8 A square has an area of 60 cm². Find the length of a side. Give your answer correct to 1 decimal place.

Chapter 21
Formulae

Exercise 21A

1 Packets of biscuits cost 80p each.
Use the rule

Cost = Number of packets of biscuits × 80

to work out the cost of 4 packets of biscuits.

2 Bob works for 40 hours at a rate of pay of £10 an hour.

Pay = Rate of pay × hours worked
Use this rule to work out Bob's pay.

3 Viv used this rule to work out the number of points gained by her favourite football team.

Number of points gained = Number of wins × 3 + Number of draws

Viv's favourite football team had 20 wins and 4 draws. Work out the number of points gained by her favourite football team.

(1388 March 2006)

4 Use the word formula

Total cost
= cost of one pie × number of pies

to work out the total cost of

a 15 pies if one pie costs 90p

b two dozen pies if one pie costs £1.20

5 Bottles of milk are stacked in crates. Use the formula

Number of bottles = Number of bottles in one crate × Number of crates

to work out the number of bottles in

a 12 crates, each containing 24 bottles

b 30 crates, each containing 18 bottles.

Exercise 21B

1 Tom buys some eggs at 45p each. Write down a word formula that Tom could use to work out the total cost of the eggs.

2 There are some chocolates in a box. The chocolates are shared equally amongst 5 people. Write down a word formula that could be used to work out the number of chocolates that each person receives.

3 Zach works for a rate of £8 an hour.

a Write down a word formula that Zach could use to work out his total pay.

b Use your formula to work out Zach's total pay when he works for 30 hours.

4 Finlay sells CDs. He is paid 50p for each CD that he sells.

a Write down a word formula that Finlay could use to work out how much he is paid.

b Use your formula to work out how much Finlay is paid when he sells 46 CDs.

5 In a hockey competition, 2 points are awarded for each win and one point is awarded for each draw.

a Write down a word formula that could be used to work out the total number of points awarded to each team.

b Use your formula to work out the total number of points awarded to a team that won 6 matches and drew 4 matches.

6 Tumi pays a fixed charge of £15 each month for her mobile phone. In addition calls are charged at 10p for each minute that she uses her phone.

a Write down a word formula which could be used to work out Tumi's phone bill.

b Tumi used her mobile phone for 200 minutes in January. Use your formula to work out Tumi's phone bill for January.

Exercise 21C

1 The formula $V = IR$ is used in science. Use this formula to work out the value of V when

a $I = 5$ and $R = 12$

b $I = 2.5$ and $R = 10$

2 $P = c - d$

Use this formula to work out the value of P when

a $c = 20, d = 7$

b $c = -4, d = 12$

3 The formula $a = \dfrac{v - u}{t}$ can be used to work out acceleration a.

Use this formula to work out the value of a when

a $v = 30, u = 20$ and $t = 2$

b $v = 45, u = 12$ and $t = 3$

4 The formula for the perimeter of a rectangle is $P = 2(l + w)$

Use this formula to find the value of P when

a $l = 5$ and $w = 3$

b $l = 8$ and $w = 2$

Exercise 21G

1 Write down whether each of the following is an expression or an identity or an equation or a formula.

 a $L = M + 7$ **b** $A = 2bh$

 c $3t + 2t = 5t$ **d** $y - 3$

 e $5s + 4 = 12$ **f** $x^3 - x^2$

 g $5pq$ **h** $\dfrac{x - 1}{2} = 5$

 i $C = 8B - 5D$

 j $6y + 4 - 2y = 4y + 4$

 k $m^2 + m - 8 = 0$

 l $v = u + at$

 m $c + 3d - 4c = 3d - 3c$

 n $x^2 + 4x - 12$

 o $7(r + 3) = 7r + 21$

 p $6a + 8b = 2(3a + 4b)$

 q $x - \dfrac{2x + 1}{3}$

Chapter 22
Circumference and area of a circle

Exercise 22A

If your calculator does not have π button, take the value of π to be 3.142
Give answers correct to 1 decimal place unless stated otherwise.

1 Work out the circumferences of circles with these diameters.

 a 13 cm **b** 31 mm **c** 4.3 m

 d 8.4 cm **e** 23.6 m

2 Work out the circumferences of circles with these radii.

 a 12 m **b** 5.6 cm **c** 11 mm

 d 6.74 m **e** 5.6 mm

3 Work out the diameters of circles with these circumferences.

 a 37 mm **b** 42 m **c** 48.5 cm

 d 54.2 cm **e** 67.36 m

4 The circumference of a circle is 37.1 m. Work out its radius.

5 The diameter of a pound coin is 22.5 mm. Work out its circumference.

6 The radius of a train engine wheel is 0.85 m. Work out its circumference correct to the nearest centimetre.

7 The circumference of a 10p coin is 77 mm. Work out its diameter.

8 A semicircle has a diameter of 7.8 cm.

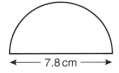

Work out its perimeter.
(Hint: the perimeter includes the diameter.)

9 A quarter circle has a radius of 5.8 cm.

Work out its perimeter.
(Hint: the perimeter includes the two radii.)

10 A shape is made from a 27 mm by 16 mm rectangle and a semicircle.

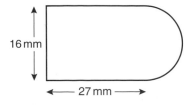

Work out its perimeter.

11 A shape is made from an 8.7 cm by 4.8 cm rectangle and a quarter circle.

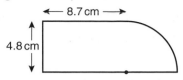

Work out its perimeter.

12 The diameter of a unicycle wheel is 60 cm. Work out the number of complete turns the wheel makes when the unicycle travels 500 metres.

Exercise 22B

If your calculator does not have a π button, take the value of π to be 3.142

Give answers correct to 1 decimal place unless stated otherwise.

1 Work out the areas of circles with these radii.

    a 5 cm   **b** 4.7 m   **c** 3.9 mm

    d 1.9 cm   **e** 2.83 m

2 Work out the areas of circles with these diameters.

    a 9 cm   **b** 11 mm   **c** 7.3 m

    d 10.3 cm   **e** 9.14 m

3 The radius of a semicircle is 3.4 cm.

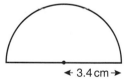

Work out its area.

4 The diameter of a semicircle is 7.5 cm.

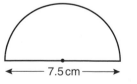

Work out its area.

5 The radius of a quarter circle is 9.3 m.

Work out its area.

9.3 m

6 A shape is made from a 4.3 m by 2.7 m rectangle and a semicircle.

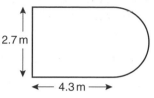

Work out its area.

7 The diagram shows an 8 cm by 5 cm rectangle inside a circle of diameter 12 cm.

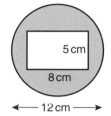

5 cm

8 cm

12 cm

Work out the area of the shaded region.

8 Swinside stone circle, in the Lake District, has a radius of 14.5 m.

    a Work out the circumference of the circle.

    b Work out the area enclosed by the circle correct to the nearest m².

Exercise 22C

In Questions **1–4**, give the answers as multiples of π.

1 Find the circumference of a circle with a diameter of 5 m.

2 Find the area of a circle with a radius of 7 cm.

3 Find the circumference of a circle with a radius of 10 cm.

4 Find the area of a circle with a diameter of 12 m.

5 The diameter of a semicircle is 6 cm. Find its perimeter.
Give your answer in terms of π.

6 The radius of a semicircle is 8 cm.
Find its area.
Give your answer as a multiple of π.

7 The diameter of a quarter circle is 40 cm.
Find its perimeter.
Give your answer in terms of π.

8 The radius of a quarter circle is 6 cm.
Find its area.
Give your answer as a multiple of π.

9 The circumference of a circle is 24π cm.
Find its diameter.

10 The diameter of an archery target is 80 cm.

   a Find its area as a multiple of π.

The diameter of the 'bull's eye' is 16 cm.

   b Find the area of the 'bull's eye' as a multiple of π.

   c Express the area of the 'bull's eye' as a fraction of the area of the whole target.

Chapter 23
Probability

Exercise 23A

1 In each of the following choose the word from the list below that best describes the probability of each outcome happening.

Impossible   Unlikely   Even chance
Likely   Certain

   a There will be 32 days in the next month.

   b The news will be on television tonight.

   c The sun will shine in spring.

   d Tuesday will be the next day after Monday.

   e An adult elephant will weigh less than a dog.

   f A card picked from a pack of playing cards will be the ace of spades.

   g It will snow in London next winter.

   h The roll of a dice will show an even number.

2 Draw a probability scale. Mark with a $\downarrow$ the probability of each of the following outcomes. Label your arrows with letters **a–e**.

   a A card picked from a pack of playing cards will be a picture card.

   b A fish will have 5 legs.

   c Next year, February will be the longest month.

   d The temperature will rise to 100° next summer.

   e The roll of a normal dice will show a number less than 7

Exercise 23B

1 A fair dice has 3 red faces, 2 blue faces and 1 green face. The dice is thrown once.
Write down the probability that the dice will land on

   a red   **b** blue   **c** green.

2 Michelle has a bag of 10 counters. 3 of the counters are black, 2 are white and the others are yellow. Michelle chooses a counter at random from the bag. Find the probability that Michelle will choose

   a a black counter

   b a white counter

   c a yellow counter.

3 A fair five-sided spinner is numbered 1 to 5 Tony spins the spinner once.

   a Find the probability that the spinner will land on the number 3

   b Find the probability that the spinner will land on a number greater than 2

   c Find the probability that the spinner will land on a multiple of 2

4 Uzma has 12 earrings in a jewellery box.
8 earrings are gold and the rest are silver.

Uzma chooses an earring at random from the jewellery box. What is the probability that this earring is

a gold

b silver

c platinum?

6 Dan has 6 cards numbered 2, 4, 5, 8, 9 and 10 Dan chooses one of the cards at random. What is the probability that the card will show

a an odd number

b an odd number less than 5

c an even number

d a factor of 10

e an even number bigger than 5

f a factor of 12?

Exercise 23C

1 The two-way table gives some information about the age and gender of members of a golf club.

	Male	Female	Total
Under 18	14	5	19
18 to 55	124	38	162
Over 55	79	23	102
Total	217	66	283

Write down the total number of

a male members

b female members over 55

c female members who are not under 18

2 The two-way table gives some information about the colours and makes of cars in a garage.

	Silver	Black	Red	Total
Ford		5	4	
Rover	8			13
Total			6	25

a Copy and complete the two-way table.

A car is chosen at random. Find the probability that the car will be

b a Rover

c a black Ford

d either silver or red.

Give your answers in their simplest form.

3 The two-way table gives some information about the maths level of students in a school.

	3	4	5	6	7	Total
Boys		28		40		170
Girls			65	56	20	
Total	21	59	129			350

a Copy and complete the two-way table.

Find the probability that a student chosen at random will be

b a boy

c a student with maths level 3

d a girl with maths level 6

Give your answers in their simplest form.

4 56 students were asked if they watched tennis yesterday. 20 of the students are boys. 17 girls watched tennis. 13 boys did not watch tennis.

	Boys	Girls	Total
Watched tennis			
Did not watch tennis			
Total			

a Use the information to complete the two-way table.

b One of these students is to be chosen at random. Write down the probability that the student chosen is a boy.

(1387 November 2005)

Exercise 23D

1 A 3-sided spinner, with sides numbered 1, 2 and 3, is spun and a dice is rolled at the same time. Draw the sample space showing all possible outcomes.

2 There are three beads in a bag. One bead is red, one bead is white and one bead is yellow.

There are also three beads in a box. One bead is green, one bead is pink and one bead is blue.

Without looking, Saskia takes, at random, one bead from the bag and one bead from the box.

One possible outcome for the colours of the two beads taken is (red, green).

List all the possible outcomes.

(1388 March 2006)

3 A fair blue dice and a fair red dice are thrown at the same time.

a Find the probability that the sum of the numbers on the two dice will be

  i 7   **ii** an even number

b Find the probability that the number on the blue dice will be greater than the number on the red dice. Give all probabilities in their simplest forms.

Exercise 23E

1 The probability that Daniel will be the player of the year is 0.68. Work out the probability that Daniel will not be the player of the year.

2 The probability that it will rain in London tomorrow is $\frac{3}{5}$. Work out the probability that it will not rain in London tomorrow.

3 Each day, Anthony travels to work. He can be on time or early or late. The probability that he will be on time is 0.02. The probability that he will be early is 0.79. Work out the probability that he will be late.

(1388 March 2006)

4 A school snack bar offers a choice of four snacks. The four snacks are burgers, pizza, pasta and salad. Students can choose one of these four snacks. The table shows the probability that a student will choose a burger or pizza or salad.

Snack	burger	pizza	pasta	salad
Probability	0.35	0.15		0.2

Work out the probability that the student

a did not choose salad

b chose pasta.   *(1387 November 2005)*

Exercise 23F

1 A dice is biased. The dice is thrown 600 times. It lands 150 times on the number 4

a Write down the relative frequency of the dice landing on the number 4

b The dice is to be thrown again. Estimate the probability that the coin will land on 4

2 A bag contains a black brick, a blue brick, a green brick and a brown brick. Eva chooses a brick at random. She does this 200 times. The table shows the number of times each of the coloured bricks are chosen.

Black	Blue	Green	Brown
52	82	28	38

a Write down the relative frequency of Eva choosing the blue brick.

b Write down the relative frequency of Eva choosing the brown brick.

Eva chooses a brick one more time. Estimate the probability that this brick will be

c i black   **ii** green.

3 The probability of a student choosing a pizza at a snack bar is 0.35

400 students used the snack bar on Friday. Work out an estimate for the number of students who chose a pizza.

(1387 November 2005)

4 A box contains 50 counters. There are 23 white counters, 19 black counters and 8 yellow counters.

Piero takes at random a single counter from the box. Work out the probability that he takes a white counter or a yellow counter

(1388 November 2005)

5 A bag contains 10 coloured sweets. Each sweet is green or orange or lemon. Viv chooses a sweet at random from the bag and then replaces it. She does this 400 times. The table shows the numbers of each coloured sweet chosen.

Green	Orange	Lemon
120	202	78

a Estimate the number of green sweets in the bag.

b Estimate the number of orange sweets in the bag.

c Estimate the number of lemon sweets in the bag.

Chapter 24
Ratio and proportion

Exercise 24A

1

Write down the ratio of

a the number of circles to the number of squares

b the number of squares to the number of triangles

c the number of triangles to the number of circles

d the number of circles to the number of squares to the number of triangles

2 For each of the following write down the ratio of the number of light blue shapes to the number of dark blue shapes. Write each ratio in its simplest form.

a

b

3 Write each ratio in its simplest form

a 6:8   b 5:10

c 12:20   d 25:40

e 32:24   f 150:200

g 500:600

4 Write each ratio in its simplest form

a £2:40p   b 30 cm:1 m

c 500 m:3 km   d 20 mm:6 cm

e 2.5 kg:750 g

5 In a class there are 14 boys and 16 girls. Write down the ratio of the number of boys to the number of girls. Write your ratio in its simplest form.

6 On a piano there are 50 white keys and 35 black keys. Write down the ratio of the number of white keys to the number of black keys. Write your ratio in its simplest form

7 A model boat has a length of 8 cm. The real boat has a length of 12 m. Write down the ratio of the length of the model boat to the length of the real boat. Write your ratio in its simplest form.

8 There are 20 sweets in a packet.
12 of the sweets are mints.
The rest of the sweets are toffees.
Write down the ratio of the number of mints to the number of toffees.
Give your ratio in its simplest form.
(1388 March 2006)

9 A recipe for cake requires 450 grams of flour and 175 grams of butter.
Write down the ratio of grams of flour to grams of butter.
Give your answer in its simplest form.
(1388 January 2003)

Exercise 24B

1 Write the following ratios in the form 1 : n

a 2:6   b 5:20   c 2:9

d 5:1   e 3:2

2 In a pencil case there are 4 pencils and 12 pens. Write down the ratio of the number of pencils to the number of pens. Write your ratio in the form 1 : n.

3 In a village there are 300 families and a total of 630 children.

  a Write down the ratio of the number of families to the number of children. Write your ratio in its simplest form.

  b Write your answer to **a** in the form $1 : n$.

4 A bag contains red beads and blue beads in the ratio 1 : 7
What fraction of the beads are **a** red **b** blue?

5 In a class the ratio of the number of girls to the number of boys is 3 : 4
What fraction of the class are boys?

6 In a drawer the ratio of the number of blue socks to the number of black socks to the number of grey socks is 5 : 7 : 2

  a What fraction of the socks are blue?

  b What fraction of the socks are grey? Write your fraction in its simplest form.

Exercise 24C

1 The ratio of the number of red beads to the number of yellow beads in a bag is 1 : 2
Work out the number of yellow beads if there are

  a 2 red beads

  b 5 red beads

  c 13 red beads

2 Purple paint is made by mixing blue paint and red paint in the ratio 2 : 3
Work out the amount of red paint needed for

  a 4 litres of blue paint

  b 10 litres of blue paint

  c 16 litres of blue paint.

3 In a garden the ratio of the number of daffodils to the number of tulips is 5 : 3

  a If there are 15 tulips in the garden, work out the number of daffodils.

  b If there are 60 daffodils in the garden, work out the number of tulips.

4 In a field the ratio of the number of horses to the number of cows is 1 : 6

  a If there are 3 horses in the field, work out the number of cows.

  b If there are 48 cows in the field, work out the number of horses.

5 On a map, 1 cm represents 4 km. What distance on the map will represent a real distance of

  a 12 km   **b** 32 km   **c** 10 km?

6 On a map, 1 cm represents 4 km. Work out the real distance between two towns if their distance apart on the map is

  a 2 cm   **b** 6 cm

  c 3.5 cm   **d** 5.3 cm

7 James uses a scale of 1 : 200 to make a scale drawing of a building.

  a On the scale drawing, the width of the building is 3 cm. What is the real width of the building?

  b On the scale drawing, the length of the building is 4.3 cm. What is the real length of the building?

8 The scale of a map is 1 : 50 000

  a On the map, the distance between two towns is 3.1 cm. Work out the real distance between the towns. Give your answer in kilometres.

  b Work out the distance on the map between two towns if the real distance between the towns is **i** 5 km **ii** 8 km

Exercise 24D

1 a Share £30 in the ratio 1 : 2

  b Share £25 in the ratio 3 : 2

2 Colin and David share £20 in the ratio 1 : 4
Work out how much each person gets.

3 A piece of wood is of length 45 cm.
The length is divided in the ratio 7 : 2
Work out the length of each part.
(1388 November 2005)

4 Alex and Ben were given a total of £240
They shared the money in the ratio 5 : 7
Work out how much money Ben received.
(1388 January 2005)

5 Ken and Susan share £20 in the ratio 1 : 3
Work out how much money each person gets.
(1388 June 2003)

6 Mrs Smith shared £375 between her two children in the ratio 1 : 4
She gave the bigger share to Kylie.
Work out how much money she gave to Kylie.

7 Derek, Erica and Fred share £108 in the ratio 3 : 4 : 2
Calculate the amount of money Erica gets.
(1388 January 2003)

8 There are 21 questions in a science test.
Each question is on biology or on chemistry or on physics.
The numbers of questions on biology, chemistry and physics are in the ratio 4 : 2 : 1
 i What fraction of the questions are on chemistry?
 ii Work out the number of questions that are on biology.
(1388 March 2006)

Exercise 24E

1 4 sweets cost 20p. Work out the cost of 7 of these sweets.

2 Richard paid 56p for 7 pencils.
The cost of each pencil was the same.
Work out the cost of 4 of these pencils.
(1388 June 2004)

3 Michael buys 3 files.
The total cost of these 3 files is £5.40
Work out the total cost of 7 of these files.
(1387 June 2005)

4 Ruth makes poached peaches.
Here is a list of ingredients for making poached peaches for 6 people.

Poached Peaches
Ingredients for 6 people
12   yellow cling peaches
1400 ml   water
130 g   granulated sugar

Ruth makes poached peaches for 9 people.
Work out the amount of each ingredient needed to make poached peaches for 9 people.
(1388 November 2005)

5 This is a list of ingredients for making a pear & almond crumble for 4 people.

Ingredients for **4** people

80 g plain flour
60 g ground almonds
90 g soft brown sugar
60 g butter
4 ripe pears

Work out the amount of each ingredient needed to make a pear & almond crumble for **10** people.
(1387 June 2004)

6 Alfie went to Spain.
He changed £400 into euros.
The exchange rate was £1 = 1.45 euros.
Work out the number of euros that Alfie got.
(1388 March 2006)

7 A student bought a pair of sunglasses in the USA.
He paid $35.50
In England, an identical pair of sunglasses costs £26.99
The exchange rate is £1 = $1.42
In which country were the sunglasses cheaper and by how much?
Show all your working.
(1388 June 2004)

Exercise 24F

1 Change 30 miles to kilometres.

2 Change 6 inches to centimetres.

3 Change 120 centimetres to feet.

4 Change 10 centimetres to inches.

5 Change 35 pints to litres.

6 Change 44 pounds to kilograms.

7 Change 180 litres to gallons.

8 Change 20 kilometres to miles

9 Change 5 kg to pounds.

(1388 June 2004)

10 A car is travelling at a speed of 60 miles per hour. Change 60 miles per hour into kilometres per hour.

Chapter 25
Three-dimensional shapes

Exercise 25A

1 Write down the mathematical name for each of these 3-D shapes.

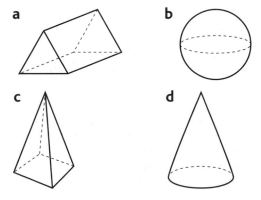

a   b

c   d

2 a For an octagonal prism, write down
  i the number of faces
  ii the number of edges
  iii the number of vertices
  b What shapes are its faces?

3 a For a decagon-based pyramid, write down
  i the number of faces
  ii the number of edges
  iii the number of vertices
  b What shapes are its faces?

Exercise 25B

1 On centimetre squared paper, draw an accurate, full-size net of a cuboid which is 4 cm by 2 cm by 1 cm.

2 Here is a net of a prism.

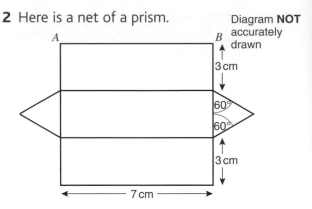

Diagram **NOT** accurately drawn

A   B
3 cm
60°
60°
3 cm
7 cm

  a Make an accurate drawing of the net.
  b Sketch the prism. *(1384 June 1997)*

3 Here is a sketch of a cylinder. Sketch a net of the cylinder.

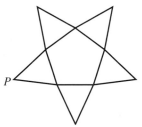

4 Here is a sketch of a net of a 3-D shape.

P

  a On a copy of the sketch, label the points which meet at *P*, when the net is folded to make the 3-D shape.
  b Sketch the 3-D shape and write down its name.
  c For the 3-D shape, write down
    i the number of vertices,
    ii the number of edges.

Exercise 25C

1 On isometric grids, make accurate, full-size drawings of
  a a cube of side 2 cm
  b a cuboid which is 5 cm by 3 cm by 1 cm.

2 On isometric grids, make accurate, full-size drawings of these 3-D shapes.
They are all prisms with the cross-sections and lengths as shown.

a
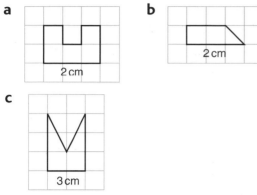
2 cm

b
2 cm

c
3 cm

3 Here is a drawing of a prism on an isometric grid.

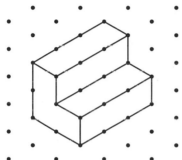

a On centimetre squared paper, draw an accurate, full-size net of the prism.
b For the prism, write down
   i the number of faces
   ii the number of vertices.

Exercise 25D

1

This solid shape is made from cubes of side one centimetre.
Find the volume of the shape.
(1385 June 2000)

2
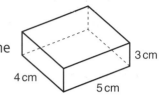
represents 1 cm³

In the solid prism, the volume of each small cube is 1 cm³. Work out the volume of the prism. *(1388 January 2005)*

3 The diagram shows a solid cuboid.
Work out the volume of the cuboid.
Give the units of your answer.

3 cm
4 cm
5 cm

4 Work out the volume of a cuboid which is 12 mm by 10 mm by 6 mm.

5 Work out the volume, in cm³, of a cuboid which is 3 m by 6 cm by 4 cm.

6 Work out the volume, in m³, of a cuboid which is 4 m by 80 cm by 5 cm.

Exercise 25E

1 The volume of a cuboid is 120 cm³. Its length is 8 cm and its width is 5 cm.
Work out its height.

2 The volume of a cuboid is 840 m³. Its length is 20 m and its height is 6 m.
Work out its width.

3 The volume of a cuboid is 1440 mm³.
Its width is 12 mm and its height is 8 mm.
Work out its length.

4 The volume of a cuboid is 140 cm³. Its length is 8 cm and its width is 5 cm.
Work out its height.

5 The volume of a cuboid is 208 m³.
Its length is 8 m and its height is 4 m.
Work out its width.

6

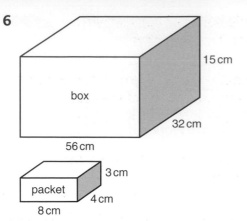

A packet is a cuboid which is 8 cm by 4 cm by 3 cm.
A box is a cuboid which is 56 cm by 32 cm by 15 cm.
Work out how many packets will fit exactly into the box.

7 A rectangular box measures 10 cm by 8 cm by 2.5 cm.
A container is a cuboid which measures 80 cm by 40 cm by 30 cm.
Work out the greatest number of boxes which can be packed in the container.

8 The volume of a cuboid is 108 cm³. Its length is 12 cm and its height is 15 mm. Work out its width. Give your answer in centimetres.

Exercise 25F

1 The diagram shows a wedge in the shape of a triangular prism.

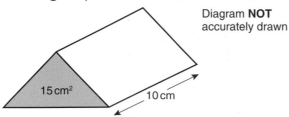

Diagram **NOT** accurately drawn

The cross-section of the prism is shown as a shaded triangle.
The area of the triangle is 15 cm².
The length of the prism is 10 cm.
Work out the volume of the prism.
(1387 June 2004)

2 The diagram shows a prism with a right-angled triangle as its cross-section.

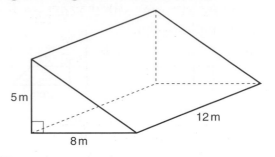

Work out the volume of the prism.

3 The shape is the cross-section of a prism 10 cm long.
Calculate the volume of the prism.
(1384 November 1997)

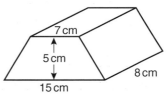

Diagram **NOT** accurately drawn

4 The diagram shows a prism.

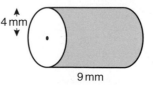

The cross-section of the prism is a trapezium.
The lengths of the parallel sides of the trapezium are 15 cm and 7 cm.
The distance between the parallel sides of the trapezium is 5 cm.
The length of the prism is 8 cm.
Work out the volume of the prism.

5 The radius of the end of a cylinder is 4 mm.

Its length is 9 mm.
Work out the volume of the cylinder.
Give your answer correct to the nearest mm³.

6 The diagram shows the cross-section of a prism.

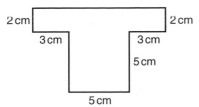

All the corners are right angles.
The length of the prism is 10 cm.
Work out the volume of the prism.

7 The cross-section of a prism is a semicircle of diameter 3.6 cm.

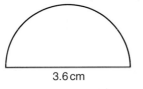

3.6 cm

The length of the prism is 9 cm.
Work out the volume of the prism.
Give your answer correct to 1 decimal place.

8 A cylindrical can has a radius of 6 centimetres.

a Calculate the area of the circular end of the can.

The capacity of the can is 2000 cm³.

b Calculate the height of the can.
Give your answer correct to 1 decimal place. *(1384 June 1995)*

Exercise 25G

1 Change

a 6.5 cm³ to mm³

b 3000 mm³ to cm³

c 800 mm³ to cm³.

2 Change

a 8 m³ to cm³

b 17 500 000 cm³ to m³

c 0.004 m³ to cm³.

3 Change

a 5000 cm³ to litres

b 24 litres to cm³

c 4.9 litres to cm³.

4 A bottle holds 0.7 litres of wine.
Change 0.7 litres to cm³.

5 The length of each side of a cube is 50 cm.
Work out the volume of the cube

a in cm³   **b** in m³.

6 A rectangular wall is 4 m wide and 2.5 m high.
One litre of paint is needed to cover the wall.
Work out the thickness of the coat of paint.
Give your answer in millimetres.

Exercise 25H

1 The following diagram represents a prism.
The cross-section (shaded region) of the prism is a right-angled isosceles triangle.
Copy the diagram and draw one plane of symmetry on the prism.

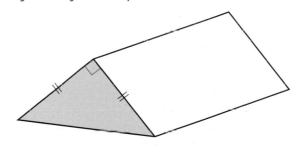

(1384 June 1995)

2 Copy these diagrams and draw in one plane of symmetry for each of these shapes.

i

ii

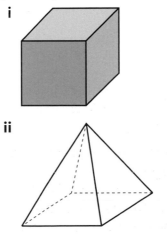

(1385 June 2000)

3

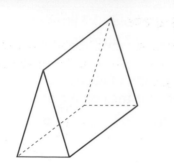

The diagram shows a sketch of a solid.
Each end of the solid is an isosceles triangle.

a Write down the name of the solid.

b For the solid,
write down
  i the number of faces
  ii the number of edges
  iii the number of vertices.

c On a copy of the diagram draw one of
the solid's planes of symmetry.

d How many planes of symmetry does the
solid have? *(1387 June 2002)*

Exercise 25I

1 Work out the surface area of

a a cube of side 10 cm

b a cuboid which is 5 cm by 4 cm by 8 cm.

2

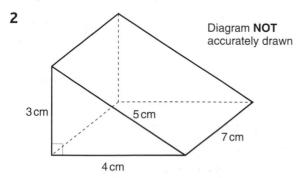

Diagram **NOT**
accurately drawn

The diagram shows a prism.
The cross-section of the prism is a right-
angled triangle.
The lengths of the sides of the triangle are
3 cm, 4 cm and 5 cm.
The length of the prism is 7 cm.

a Work out the volume of the prism.

b Work out the total surface area of the
prism. *(4400 November 2004)*

3

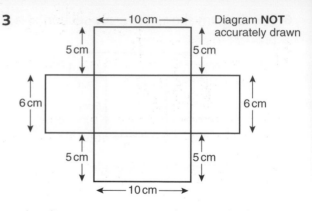

Diagram **NOT**
accurately drawn

The diagram represents the net of a box
without a lid.

a Calculate the total area of the net.

b Calculate the volume of the box.
(1384 November 1996)

4

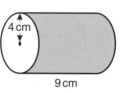

The radius of the end of a solid cylinder is
4 cm. Its length is 9 cm.
Work out the total surface area of the cylinder.
Give your answer correct to the nearest cm^2.

Exercise 25J

1 x, y and z represent lengths.
For each of these expressions, state whether
it could represent a length, an area, a
volume or none of these.
(Numbers have no dimensions.)

a x^2y **b** $2y + 3z$ **c** $xy + z$

d πyz **e** $x(y + z)$ **f** $\dfrac{xy}{z}$

2 x, y and z represent lengths.
Here are some expressions.

$2xy + 3yz$ $x^2(y + z)$ $\dfrac{x^2y}{z}$

$x^2 + 5y$ $\pi x + 4yz$ $\dfrac{xyz}{6}$

a Write down the expressions which could represent an area.

b Write down the expressions which could represent a volume.

3 The expressions below can be used to calculate lengths, area or volumes of some shapes.

The letters p, q and r represent lengths.
π and 2 are numbers which have no dimension.

Write down the three expressions that can be used to calculate an area.

$$\pi(p + q) \qquad \frac{pq}{r} \qquad rq(p + q) \qquad \pi pq$$

$$\frac{p^2 r}{2} \qquad 2r \qquad \frac{qr}{2} \qquad r(p + q)$$

$$\frac{p^2 \pi}{r} \qquad \frac{\pi pqr}{2} \qquad (1385 \text{ June } 2001)$$

4 Here are some expressions.

$\dfrac{\pi r^2}{x}$	$\pi(r + x)$	$\pi r + r$	$\dfrac{\pi r^3}{x}$	$\pi r^2 + rx$	$\dfrac{r^2}{\pi x}$

The letters r and x represent lengths. π is a number which has no dimension.

Two of the expressions could represent areas.

a Copy the table and tick the boxes (✓) underneath the two expressions which could represent areas.

Here are four more expressions.

πr^3	$\pi r^4 + \pi x$	$\dfrac{\pi r^4}{x}$	$\pi r^2 + \pi r x$

One of these four expressions cannot represent a length or an area or a volume.

b Copy the table and put a cross in the box (✗) underneath the one expression which cannot represent a length or an area or a volume.

c Rearrange the formula $y = r + 3x$ to make x the subject.

(1385 November 2001)

Exercise 25K

1 On centimetre squared paper, draw the plan, front elevation and side elevation for this prism.

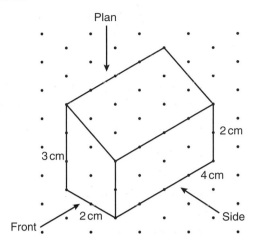

2 Draw a sketch of the plan, front elevation and side elevation of this solid.

3 Here are the plan, front elevation and side elevation of a 3-D shape.
On isometric paper, draw the prism.

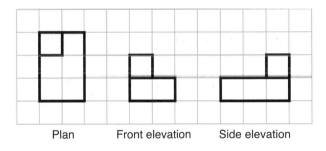

Plan   Front elevation   Side elevation

Exercise 25L

1 a Write down the coordinates of P, Q and R.

b Write down the coordinates of the midpoint of QR.

2

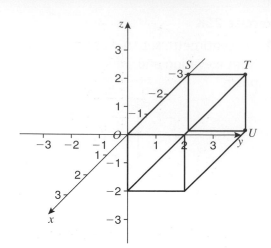

a Write down the coordinates of S, T and U.

b Write down the coordinates of the midpoint of ST.

c Write down the coordinates of the midpoint of TU.

3 The coordinates of five of the corners of a cube are $(0, 0, 0)$, $(2, 0, 0)$, $(2, 2, 0)$, $(0, 2, 0)$ and $(0, 0, 2)$. Find the coordinates of the other three corners.

4 The coordinates of five of the corners of a cuboid are $(1, 3, -2)$, $(1, 3, 1)$, $(1, -2, 1)$, $(1, -2, -2)$ and $(-4, 3, -2)$. Find the coordinates of the other three corners.

5 A is the point $(2, 2, 0)$. B is the point $(0, 0, 6)$. Find the coordinates of the midpoint of AB.

Chapter 26
Transformations

Exercise 26A

1 a Make a copy of shape **T** in the middle of a grid of centimetre squares.

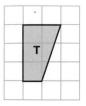

b On your grid, translate shape **T**
  i 3 to the right and 2 up and label your new shape **A**
  ii 2 to the right and 4 down and label your new shape **B**
  iii by the vector $\begin{pmatrix} 1 \\ 4 \end{pmatrix}$ and label your new shape **C**
  iv by the vector $\begin{pmatrix} -2 \\ 6 \end{pmatrix}$ and label your new shape **D**
  v by the vector $\begin{pmatrix} -4 \\ -3 \end{pmatrix}$ and label your new shape **E**.

2

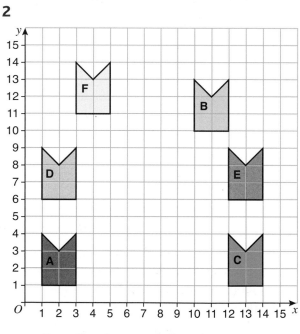

a Describe the translation that maps
  i shape **A** onto shape **B**
  ii shape **A** onto shape **C**
  iii shape **A** onto shape **D**
  iv shape **F** onto shape **E**
  v shape **C** onto shape **D**
  vi shape **F** onto shape **D**

b What is true about the translation that maps shape **D** to shape **A** and the translation that maps
  i shape **E** to shape **C**
  ii shape **C** to shape **E**?

Exercise 26B

1 Copy the diagram and rotate the triangle a half turn about the point O.

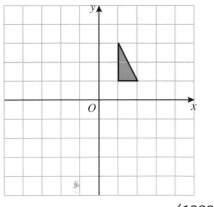

(1388 April 2005)

2 Copy the diagram and rotate the triangle a quarter turn anticlockwise about the point O.

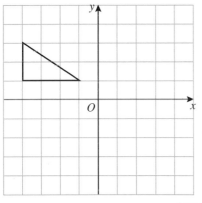

(1388 April 2006)

3 Copy the following diagram and on the grid rotate triangle **A** 180° about O.
Label your new triangle **B**.

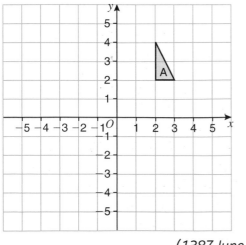

(1387 June 2003)

4

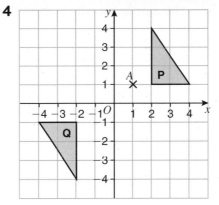

a Describe fully the single transformation that maps shape **P** onto shape **Q**.

b On a copy of this diagram, rotate shape **P** 90° anticlockwise about the point $A(1, 1)$. Label the new shape **R**.

(1385 June 2000)

5

a On a copy of the diagram, rotate triangle **P** 90° clockwise about the point $(0, 2)$. Label the new triangle **Q**.

b On the same diagram, translate triangle **P** by the vector $\begin{pmatrix} 5 \\ -6 \end{pmatrix}$.

Label the new triangle **R**.

(1388 November 2005)

6 Describe fully the **single** transformation that maps **P** onto **Q**.

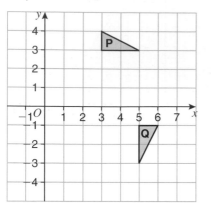

(4400 November 2005)

Exercise 26C

1 On a copy of this diagram, draw the reflection of this shape in the mirror line.

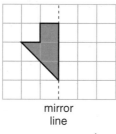

mirror
line

(1385 June 2000)

2 A shaded shape is shown on the grid of centimetre squares.

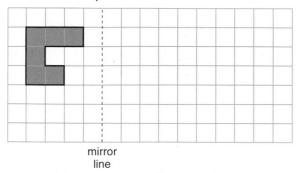

mirror
line

a Work out the perimeter of the shaded shape.

b Work out the area of the shaded shape.

c On a copy of this diagram, reflect the shaded shape in the mirror line.

(1387 June 2003)

3 On a copy of this diagram, reflect the triangle in the *x*-axis.

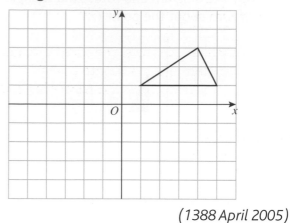

(1388 April 2005)

4 Triangle **A** and triangle **B** have been drawn on the grid.

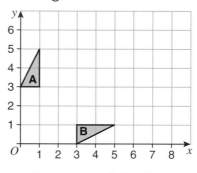

a On a copy of the diagram,
  i reflect triangle **A** in the line $x = 3$
    Label this image **C**.
  ii reflect triangle **B** in the line $y = 2$
    Label this image **D**.

b Describe fully the single transformation which will map triangle **A** onto triangle **B**.

(1387 June 2005)

5 Triangle **B** is a reflection of triangle **A**.

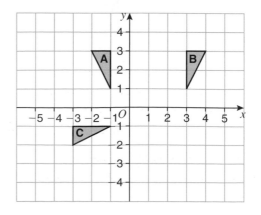

a **i** On a copy of the diagram, draw the mirror line for this reflection.
  ii Write down the equation of the mirror line.

b Describe fully the single transformation that maps triangle **A** onto triangle **C**.

(1385 November 2002)

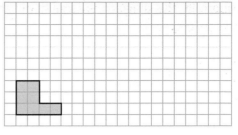

(1388 January 2004)

Exercise 26D

1

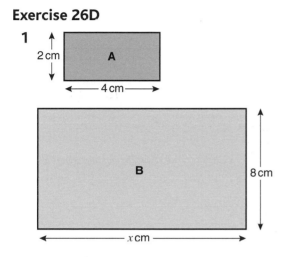

Rectangle **B** is an enlargement of rectangle **A**.

a Work out the scale factor of the enlargement.

b Work out the value of x

2 A shape has been drawn on a grid of centimetre squares.

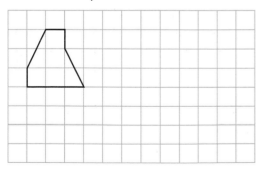

a Work out the area of the shape.

b On a copy of the diagram, enlarge the shape with a scale factor of 2

(5540 June 2005)

3 On a copy of this diagram, draw an enlargement, scale factor 3, of the shaded shape.

4

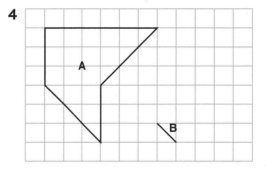

Shape **A** is shown in the diagram.
Shape **A** is enlarged to obtain the shape **B**.
Shape **B** is shown incomplete in the diagram.

a Write down the scale factor of the enlargement.

b On a copy of this diagram, complete the drawing of shape **B**.   *(1384 June 1997)*

Exercise 26E

1 On a copy of this diagram, enlarge the shaded triangle by a scale factor 2, centre O.

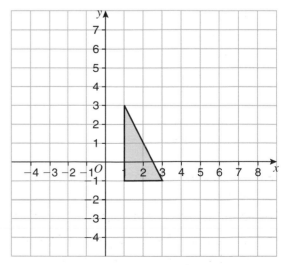

(1387 June 2004)

2 On a copy of this diagram, enlarge the shaded triangle by a scale factor of 2, centre C.

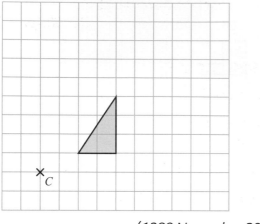

(1388 November 2005)

3

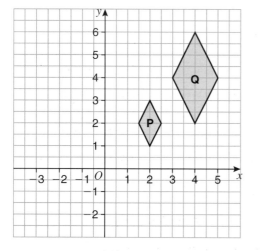

i Describe fully the single transformation that maps shape **P** onto shape **Q**.

ii On a copy of this diagram, reflect shape **P** in the line $x = 1$

(1387 November 2004)

4 On a copy of this diagram, enlarge triangle **P** with scale factor $\frac{1}{2}$ and centre (4, 2).

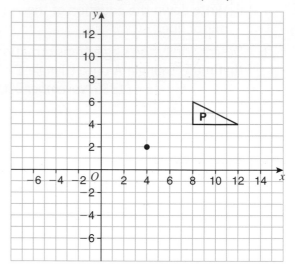

(4400 November 2005)

5

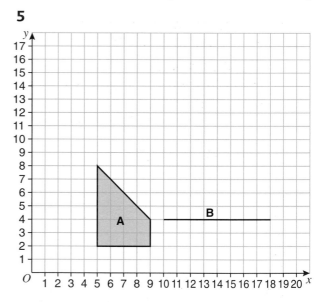

Shape **A** is shown on the grid.

Shape **A** is enlarged, centre (0, 0), to obtain shape **B**.

One side of shape **B** has been drawn for you.

a Write down the scale factor of the enlargement.

b On a copy of this diagram, complete shape **B**.

The shape **A** is enlarged by scale factor $\frac{1}{2}$ centre (5, 16) to give the shape **C**.

c On the copy of this diagram, draw shape **C**. *(1385 November 2001)*

6 On a copy of this diagram,

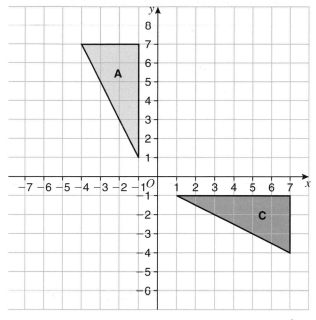

a enlarge triangle **A** by the scale factor $\frac{1}{3}$ with centre the point $P(-7, 7)$.

b describe fully the single transformation which maps triangle **A** onto triangle **C**.

(1385 November 2000)

7 On a copy of this diagram

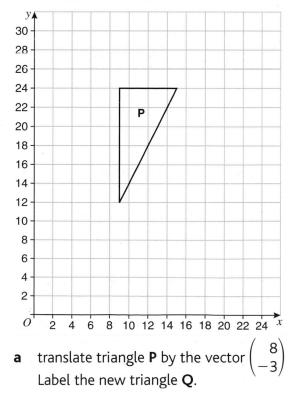

a translate triangle **P** by the vector $\begin{pmatrix} 8 \\ -3 \end{pmatrix}$. Label the new triangle **Q**.

b enlarge triangle **P** by a scale factor of $\frac{1}{3}$, centre $(15, 6)$. Label the new triangle **R**.

(1388 April 2005)

Chapter 27
Algebra 2

Exercise 27A

Simplify

1 $p \times p \times p \times p + p \times p \times p \times p$

2 $3a \times a \times a - a \times a \times a$

3 $x^5 \times x^2$ **4** $n \times n^4$

5 $q^3 \times q$ **6** $y^8 \div y^2$

7 $q^5 \div q$ **8** $6x^3 \times x^8$

9 $y^5 \times 3y^4$ **10** $3q \times 2q^6$

11 $2 \times 3r^7 \times 7r$ **12** $6x^4 \div x^2$

13 $15p^9 \div 5p^5$ **14** $8p \div 2p$

15 $y \times y^5 \times y^6$ **16** $5x^3 \times x \times 2x^3$

17 $4q \times 5q^2 \times 2q^4$

18 $(4 \times x \times x^3) + (x^6 \div x^2)$

19 $(24y^6 \div 2y^2) - (3y^3 \times 2y)$

20 $(4x^3 \times 4x^3) + (8x^{10} \div 2x^4)$
     $- (2x^2 \times 2x^2 \times 2x^2)$

Exercise 27B

1 Work out the value of each of these expressions when $x = -2$

   a $x^2 + 3$ **b** $x^3 - 4x$ **c** $x^4 + 2x^2$

   d $x^5 - 3x$ **e** $x^6 + 2x^3$

2 Tanya said "When $x = -3$, then the value of $4x^2$ is 144".

Toni said "When $x = -3$, then the value of $4x^2$ is 36".

   a Who is right? Explain why.

   b Work out the value of $4(x + 1)^2$ when $x = -3$

3 Work out the value of $3xy - 4x + 3y^2$ when $x = -1$ and $y = 2$

4 Work out the value of each of these expressions, when $a = -3$ and $b = -2$

  a $ab + 3$ **b** $ab^2 + 2b$

  c $a^2 - b^2 + 3a$ **d** $2a^2b^2 - 5b$

  e $a^3 - b^3 + 2a - 3b$

5 Work out the value of the expression $4a^2 - 7a$ when $a = -5$

6 Work out the value of the expression $x^3 + 5x^2 - 2x$ when $x = -3$

7 Work out the value of these expressions when $a = -2$

  a $\dfrac{6a^4}{a^2}$ **b** $5a^2 + 8a - 7$

  c $\dfrac{6a^2 + 8a^3}{a^2}$ **d** $\dfrac{5a^3 + 4a}{3a}$

8 Work out the value of the expression $4(x + 2)^3$ when $x = -5$

Exercise 27C

1 Multiply out

  a $x(x + 2)$ **b** $y(y - 3)$

  c $2a(a + 1)$ **d** $b(6 - 5b)$

  e $c(7c + c^2)$ **f** $d(2e - d)$

  g $-3(x + 2)$ **h** $-(x - 4)$

  i $-4(3y^2 - 2y)$ **j** $-2(a^2 - 3a - 4)$

2 Expand and simplify $5(2x + 3) - 2(x - 1)$
                     (1385 May 2002)

3 Expand and simplify $2(3x + 4) - 3(4x - 5)$
                    (1387 June 2003)

4 Expand and simplify

  a $6x - 5(x + 2)$

  b $7y - 4(y - 3)$

  c $9a - 2(3a + 4)$

  d $4b - 1 - 6(b - 2)$

  e $x(x + 3) + 2(x + 1)$

  f $y(y + 4) - 2(y + 1)$

  g $z(z - 4) - (z - 3)$

  h $k(k + 5) - 6(k - 2)$

5 Expand and simplify $(y + 3)(y + 4)$
                    (1388 March 2006)

6 Expand and simplify

  a $(x + 4)(x + 1)$ **b** $(y + 3)(y + 7)$

  c $(z + 2)(z - 1)$ **d** $(x + 5)(x - 7)$

  e $(x - 2)(x + 8)$ **f** $(x - 9)(x + 4)$

  g $(x - 1)(x - 3)$ **h** $(x - 5)(x - 4)$

  i $(x + 2)(x - 2)$ **j** $(y + 1)^2$

  k $(3 - x)^2$

Exercise 27D

Factorise

  1 $ap + aq$ **2** $2cd + ed$

  3 $3ab - bc$ **4** $p - 2qp$

  5 $2cd - 3de + 4d$ **6** $y^2 - 8y$

  7 $x^2 + x$ **8** $k - k^2$

  9 $3y + y^2$ **10** $2y^2 + 3y$

  11 $7y - 4y^2$ **12** $x^3 - 3x$

  13 $2x^3 + 3x$ **14** $t^2 + pt - 8t$

  15 $x^3 - x^2 - 7x$

Exercise 27E

Solve these equations:

  1 $x^2 = 36$ **2** $2x^2 = 2$

  3 $3x^2 = 48$ **4** $x^2 + 24 = 49$

  5 $x^2 - 16 = 9$ **6** $x^2 + 1 = 82$

  7 $5y^2 = 45$ **8** $9y^2 = 81$

  9 $4y^2 = 100$ **10** $51 + x^2 = 100$

Exercise 27F

1 Tariq and Yousef have been asked to find the solution, correct to one decimal place, of the equation $x^3 + 2x = 56$

  a Work out the value of $x^3 + 2x$ when $x = 3.65$

Tariq says 3.6 is the solution. Yousef says 3.7 is the solution.

  b Use your answer to part **a** to decide whether Tariq or Yousef is correct. You must give a reason.

(1388 March 2006)

2 The equation $x^3 - x = 20$ has a solution between 2 and 3. Use a trial and improvement method to find this solution. Give your answer correct to one decimal place. You must show **ALL** your working.

(1388 January 2004)

3 The equation $x^3 + 10x = 21$ has a solution between 1 and 2. Use a trial and improvement method to find this solution. Give your answer correct to one decimal place. You must show **ALL** your working.

(1387 November 2005)

4 The equation $x^3 + 2x = 65$ has a solution between 3 and 4. Use a trial and improvement method to find this solution. Give your solution correct to one decimal place. You must show **ALL** your working.

(1388 November 2005)

5 a Show that the equation $y^3 = 4y^2 + 20$ has a solution between 4 and 5

  b Use a trial and improvement method to find this solution. Give your answer correct to **two** decimal places.

6 Use a trial and improvement method to find the solution of the equation $\dfrac{1}{x} = x^2 + 1$ that lies between 0 and 1. Give your answer correct to one decimal place.

Chapter 28
Accuracy and estimation

Exercise 28A

1 Write each number correct to the nearest integer.

a 6.4		**b** 18.2	
c 14.7		**d** 19.9	
e 0.84		**f** 128.4	
g 89.7		**h** 99.6	

2 Round each number correct to 1 significant figure.

a 44	**b** 58	**c** 6.3			
d 11.7	**e** 215	**f** 4624			
g 0.052	**h** 0.0089	**i** 1.06			

3 Work out an estimate for each of the following.

a 2.1×4.9	**b** 5.1×6.7
c 11.8×9.7	**d** 42×38
e 19.1×38.9	**f** 96.8×212
g 11.1^2	**h** 121×39
i 11.8×978	**j** 123×19.7

4 Work out an estimate for each of the following.

a 2.3×0.48	**b** 37×0.79
c 28×0.96	**d** 38×0.044
e 202.7×0.032	

5 Work out an estimate of each of the following.

a $18.4 \div 1.9$	**b** $38.2 \div 9.9$
c $44.7 \div 3.9$	**d** $484 \div 98$
e $6284 \div 2.2$	

6 Work out an estimate of each of the following.

  a $\dfrac{6.4 \times 8.2}{4.8}$ **b** $\dfrac{5.6 \times 4.4}{2.1}$

  c $\dfrac{18 \times 21.2}{39.8}$ **d** $\dfrac{614 \times 42.2}{80.8}$

  e $\dfrac{18.4 \times 22.3}{3.8 \times 5.1}$

7 Work out an estimate of each of the following.

a $\dfrac{6.3}{2.2} + 19.1$ **b** $\dfrac{15.8}{2.3} + \dfrac{32.1}{3.3}$

c $\dfrac{612}{3.2 \times 5.8}$ **d** $\dfrac{58 \times 32}{4.6 + 4.4}$

e $\dfrac{27.2 + 28.4}{1.6 \times 2.4}$

Exercise 28B

1 The weight of a can of peas is 419.6 grams. Estimate the total weight of 21 cans of peas.

2 The cost of a theatre ticket is £18.85 Estimate the total cost of 23 tickets.

3 A school has 62 classrooms. Each classroom has 18 tables. Estimate the number of tables in all the classrooms.

4 138 students pay a total of £1492 for their yearbooks. Estimate the cost of one yearbook.

5 Paint costs £2.12 per litre. Jenny pays £61.48 for paint. Estimate how many litres she buys.

6 Asif earns £312 each week. Estimate how much he will earn in a year.

7 A crate weighs 18.8 kg. Estimate the weight of 28 crates.

A van can carry a weight of 600 kg safely. Explain whether the van can safely carry 28 crates.

8 A rectangular field has a length of 58.6 m and a width of 41.2 m.

a Estimate the area of the field.

b Estimate the perimeter of the field.

9 At a football match there were 11 220 adults and 3723 children. Each adult paid £18.20 and each child paid £11.20. Estimate the total amount paid at the football match.

Exercise 28C

1 The cost of a litre of petrol is 105.9p. Work out the cost of 22.6 litres of petrol.

2 The cost of electricity is 13.369p for each unit. Work out the cost of 1225 units.

3 A glass holds 125 ml of wine. How many glasses can be completely filled from a box holding 3400 ml of wine?

4 A sales rep receives 37.9p for every mile that he drives. Work out how much he should receive when he drives 824 miles.

5 How many pieces of wire, each 75 cm long, can be cut from a coil of wire $9\frac{1}{2}$ metres long?

6 A bus can carry 56 passengers. How many buses are needed to carry 850 passengers?

7 4. 6 metres of silver wire cost £4.86. Find the cost of 6.86 metres of silver wire.

8 A storage tank holds 200 000 litres of liquid. How many containers, each holding 475 litres can be filled from the storage tank?

9 A car travels at an average speed of 60 miles per hour. Work out how far it travels in

a 2 hours 30 minutes

b 3 hours 20 minutes

10 A lorry travels at an average speed of 80 km/h. Work out the time it takes the lorry to travel

a 180 km   **b** 210 km

Exercise 28D

1 The product of two numbers is 238. One number is 3 more than the other. Use trial and improvement to find the two numbers.

2 The area of a rectangle is 528 m². The length of the rectangle is 2 m more than the width. Use trial and improvement to find the length and the width.

3 The product of three consecutive numbers is 3360. Use trial and improvement to find the 3 numbers.

4 Joanne's pay increased by 10% to £264. Use trial and improvement to find her pay before the increase.

5 Alan's house uses 1248 units of electricity. Each unit costs 49.3p. VAT is charged at 5%. Find the total amount that Alan has to pay.

6 Josh buys a car using an easy repayment plan. The plan is a deposit of 22.5% of the cash price plus 36 repayments of £249. The cash price is £8800. Work out how much Josh will pay using the easy repayment plan.

7 Calculators cost £3.28 each. There is a discount of $2\frac{1}{2}$% on the total cost if 50 or more calculators are bought. Work out the discount when 56 calculators are bought.

8 Hector buys a television. The list price of the television is £499. The total price is the list price plus VAT at 17.5%. Hector pays a deposit of 22.5% of the total price. Work out how much he pays as a deposit.

9 Alistair sells books. He sells each book for £7.60 plus VAT at $17\frac{1}{2}$%. He sells 1650 books. Work out how much money Alistair receives.
(1387 June 2005)

Exercise 28E

1 The length of a pen is 13 cm correct to the nearest cm.
   a Write down the smallest length it could be.
   b Write down the greatest length it could be.

2 The distance from London to Newcastle is 456 km correct to the nearest km.
   a Write down the smallest distance it could be.
   b Write down the longest distance it could be.

3 The mass of a block is 60 grams correct to the nearest gram.
   a Write down the smallest mass it could be.
   b Write down the largest mass it could be.

4 A pencil has a length of 12 cm correct to the nearest cm.
A pencil case has a length of 123 mm correct to the nearest mm.
Explain why the pencil might not fit inside the pencil case.

5 A circle has a radius of 5 cm correct to the nearest cm.
A square has a side of 10 cm correct to the nearest cm.
Explain why the circle might not fit inside the square.

Chapter 29
Constructions and loci

Exercise 29A

1 Draw a line *AB* 3.5 cm long. Construct an equilateral triangle with base *AB*.

2 Draw a circle, radius 2.5 cm and construct a regular hexagon inside it.

In Questions **3**–**7**, copy the diagrams onto centimetre squared paper.

3

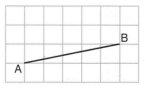

Construct the perpendicular bisector of the line *AB*.

4

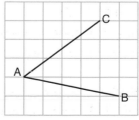

Construct the bisector of the acute angle *BAC*.

5

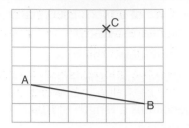

Construct the perpendicular from the point C to the line AB.

6

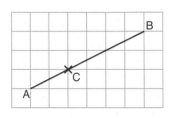

Construct the perpendicular from the point C to the line AB.

7

Construct the perpendicular at B to the line AB.

8 Construct an angle of 45°.

Exercise 29B

Copy the diagrams onto centimetre squared paper.

1

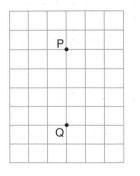

a   Draw the locus of all points which are equidistant from P and Q.

b   On the same diagram, draw the locus of all points which are 1 cm from P.

2

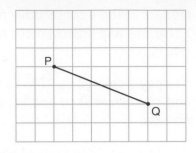

Draw the locus of all points which are 2 cm away from the line PQ.

3

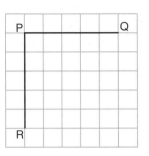

Draw the locus of points which are equidistant from two fixed lines PQ and PR.

4

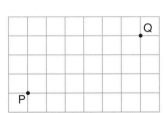

Construct accurately the locus of all the points which are equidistant from P and Q.

5

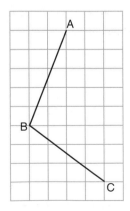

Construct accurately the locus of the points which are the same distance from BA as they are from BC.

6

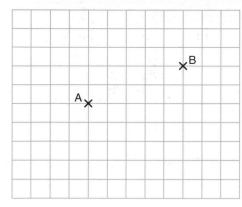

A point Q is 4 cm from A and 3 cm from B. Find the two possible positions of Q. Mark each position with a cross.

7

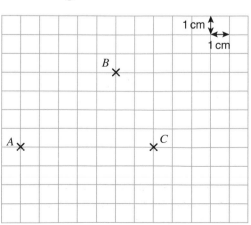

A point R is 1 cm from the line AB and 2 cm from the point C. Find the two possible positions of R. Mark each position with a cross.

8

Draw the locus of the points outside the rectangle which are 2 cm from the outside of the rectangle.

9

a On the grid, construct accurately, the locus of all points which are equidistant from A and B.

b On the grid, construct accurately the locus of all points which are 3 cm from C.
(1384 November 1997)

Exercise 29C

Make new copies of the diagrams used in questions **1–7** Exercise 29B and use them to answer questions **1–7** in this exercise.

1 a A point moves so that it is always less than 1 cm from P.
Show, by shading, the region which satisfies this condition.

b A point moves so that it is always nearer Q than P.
Show, by shading, the region which satisfies this condition.

2 A point moves so that it is always 2 cm away from the line PQ.
Show, by shading, the region which satisfies this condition.

3 A point moves so that it is always nearer PR than PQ.
Show, by shading, the region which satisfies this condition.

4 A point moves so that it is always nearer P than Q.
Show, by shading, the region which satisfies this condition.

5 A point moves so that it is always nearer AB than AC.
Show, by shading, the region which satisfies this condition.

6 A point moves so that it is always more than 4 cm from A and also less than 3 cm from B.
Show, by shading, the region which satisfies both these conditions.

7 A point moves so that it is always less than 1 cm from the line AB and also less than 2 cm from the point C.
Show, by shading, the region which satisfies both these conditions.

8

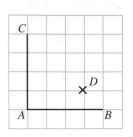

A point P moves so that it is always nearer AC than AB and also less than 2 cm from D.
Copy the diagram onto centimetre squared paper. Show, by shading, the region which satisfies both these conditions.

9 The diagram shows three points A, B and C on a centimetre grid. Copy the diagram onto centimetre squared paper.

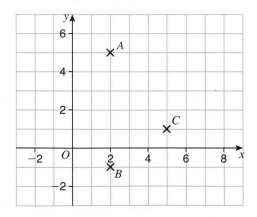

a Draw the locus of points which are equidistant from A and B.

b Draw the locus of points which are 3 cm from C.

c On the grid, shade the region in which points are nearer to A than B and also less than 3 cm from C.

(1388 January 2004)

Chapter 30
Scatter graphs

Exercise 30A

1 The table shows the number of donkey rides at Blackpool beach and the number of hours of sunshine on each of 10 days.

Number of donkey rides	Number of hours of sunshine
130	3
170	3.5
185	4
210	5
220	5.5
250	6
260	7.5
310	8.5
325	9
345	9.5

a The first 6 points in the table have been plotted on the scatter graph.
Copy and complete the scatter graph.

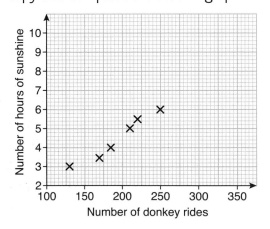

b Describe the relationship between the number of donkey rides and the number of hours of sunshine.

2 The table shows the hours of sunshine and the rainfall, in mm, in 10 towns during last summer.

Sunshine (hours)	Rainfall (mm)
650	10
455	20
560	15
430	29
620	24
400	28
640	14
375	30
520	25
620	20

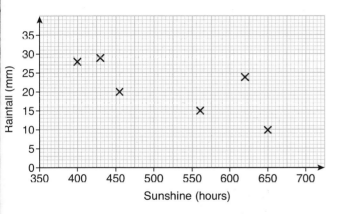

The points for the first six results in the table have been plotted on a scatter diagram.

a Copy and complete the scatter diagram.

b Describe the relationship between the hours of sunshine and the rainfall.

(1385 June 2001)

3 The table shows, for each month of last year, the average midday temperature, in °C, and the number of visitors, in thousands, to a country park.

Average midday temperature in °C	Number of visitors in thousands
3	6
6	6
9	8
11	9
12	12
18	16
21	20
23	20
19	18
15	13
8	7
4	4

a Draw a scatter graph to show the information in the table.

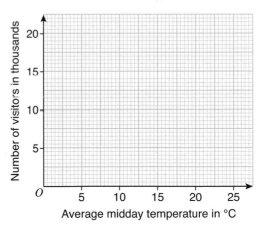

b Describe the relationship between the average midday temperature and the number of visitors.

Exercise 30B

1 10 students each took a French test and a German test. The table shows their marks.

French mark	German mark
44	48
30	35
40	45
50	54
14	18
20	22
32	36
34	38
20	25
45	50

The first 8 points in the table have been plotted on the scatter graph.

a Copy and complete the scatter graph.

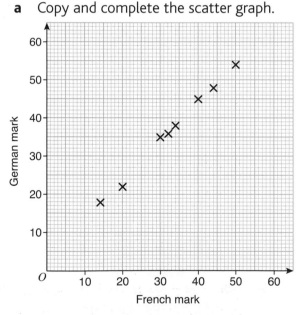

b What type of correlation does this scatter graph show?

c Draw a line of best fit on the scatter diagram.

d Use your line of best fit to estimate
  i the German mark for a student with a French mark of 26
  ii the French mark for a student with a German mark of 43

(1387 November 2005)

2 Information about oil was recorded each year for 12 years.
The table shows the amount of oil produced (in billions of barrels) and the average price of oil (in £ per barrel).

Amount of oil produced (billions of barrels)	Average price of oil (£ per barrel)
7.0	34
11.4	13
10.8	19
11.3	12
9.6	23
8.2	33
7.7	30
10.9	12.5
8.0	28.5
9.9	13.5
9.2	26.5
9.4	15.5

a Draw a scatter graph to show the information in the table.

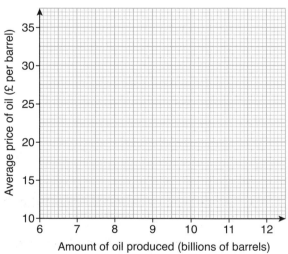

b Describe the correlation between the average price of oil and the amount of oil produced.

c Draw a line of best fit on the scatter graph.

In another year the amount of oil produced was 10.4 million barrels.

d Use your line of best fit to estimate the average price of oil per barrel in that year.

(1384 June 1997)

3 The table shows the miles per gallon (mpg) and the size of engine (in cm³) of 13 cars.

Miles per gallon (mpg)	Engine size (cm³)
18	4800
23	4000
24	4900
27	3900
28	3200
34	1900
34	2400
35	3400
42	1100
42	1400
42	2500
48	1100
50	1800

a Draw a scatter graph to show the information in the table.

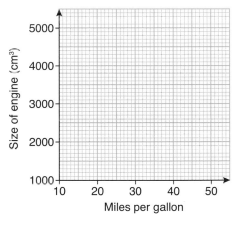

b What type of correlation does the graph have?

c Draw a line of best fit on the scatter graph.

A new car is made with an engine size of 3500 cm³.

d Use your line of best fit to estimate the miles per gallon for this car.

(1384 November 1994)

4 The table shows the body temperature, in °C, and the pulse rate, in beats/min of 10 animals.

Body temperature (°C)	Pulse rate (beats/min)
36.5	30
38.6	50
37.5	160
36.7	110
39.7	80
38	40
39	200
38	80
38.9	100
37	70

a Draw a scatter graph to show the information in the table.

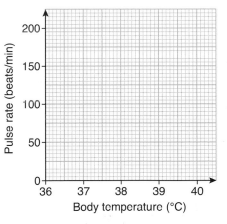

b Which of these terms best describes the relationship between body temperature and pulse rate?

positive correlation
negative correlation   zero correlation

Chapter 31
Pythagoras' theorem

Exercise 31A

In this exercise give answers in cm, correct to 1 decimal place where appropriate.

1 Work out the length of the sides marked with letters in these triangles.

a

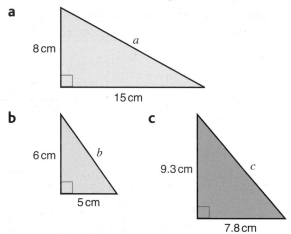

8 cm

a

15 cm

b

6 cm

b

5 cm

c

9.3 cm

c

7.8 cm

2 Work out the length of the sides marked with letters in these triangles.

a

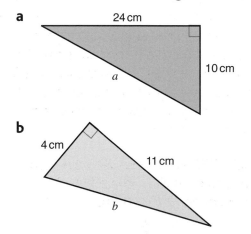

24 cm

a

10 cm

b

4 cm

11 cm

b

3 a In triangle ABC, angle $C = 90°$, $AC = 6.0$ cm and $CB = 8.5$ cm. Work out the length of AB.

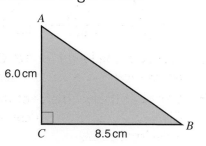

A

6.0 cm

C   8.5 cm   *B*

b In triangle PQR, angle $P = 90°$, $PR = 4.3$ cm and $PQ = 9.7$ cm. Work out the length of QR.

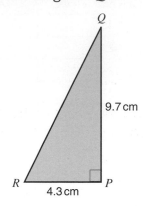

Q

9.7 cm

R   4.3 cm   *P*

c In triangle XYZ, angle $X = 90°$, $XY = 13.2$ cm and $XZ = 11.8$ cm. Work out the length of YZ.

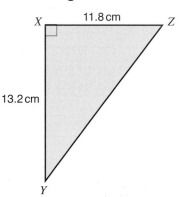

X   11.8 cm   *Z*

13.2 cm

Y

d In triangle DEF, angle $D = 90°$, $DE = 5.7$ cm and $DF = 6.8$ cm.
 i Show this information on a sketch of triangle DEF.
 ii Work out the length of EF.

Exercise 31B

In this exercise give answers in cm, correct to 1 decimal place where appropriate.

1 Work out the length of the sides marked with letters in these triangles.

a

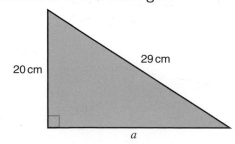

20 cm

29 cm

a

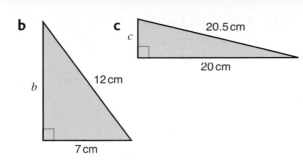

b

c

20.5 cm

12 cm

b

7 cm

2 Work out the length of the sides marked with letters in these triangles.

a

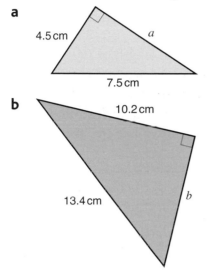

4.5 cm

a

7.5 cm

b

10.2 cm

13.4 cm

b

3 a In triangle ABC, angle $A = 90°$, $BC = 15.7$ cm and $AB = 12.8$ cm. Work out the length of AC.

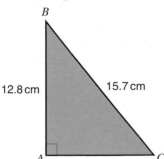

B

12.8 cm   15.7 cm

A   *C*

b In triangle XYZ, angle $Z = 90°$, $XY = 20.1$ cm and $YZ = 7.3$ cm. Work out the length of XZ.

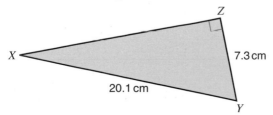

Z

X

7.3 cm

20.1 cm

Y

c In triangle PQR, angle $Q = 90°$, $PR = 12.8$ cm and $PQ = 6.2$ cm.
  i Show this information on a sketch of triangle PQR.
  ii Work out the length of QR.

Exercise 31C

1 Work out the length of the sides marked with letters in these triangles. Give your answers in cm correct to 2 decimal places.

a

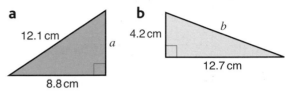

12.1 cm

a

8.8 cm

b

4.2 cm

b

12.7 cm

2 The diagram shows a sign outside a florist's shop. The sign is rectangular and is supported as shown by a cable of length 3 m. The sign rests against a vertical wall so that the top edge of the sign is horizontal. The cable is fixed to the wall a vertical distance of 2 m above this top edge. Work out the length L of the top edge of the sign. Give your answer in m correct to 2 decimal places.

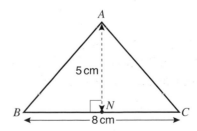

3 m   2 m

L

Flowers

3 Triangle ABC is isosceles with $AB = AC$. The midpoint of BC is the point N. $AN = 5$ cm and $BC = 8$ cm.

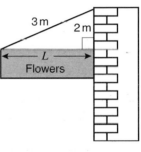

A

5 cm

B   *N*   *C*

8 cm

a Work out the length of AB. Give your answer in cm correct to 1 decimal place.

b Work out the perimeter of the triangle. Give your answer in cm correct to 1 decimal place.

4 *A* is the point with coordinates (2, 5)
B is the point with coordinates (8, 13)

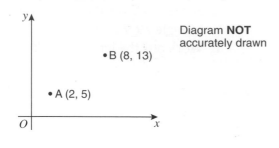

Diagram **NOT** accurately drawn

Calculate the length of *AB*.

(1388 April 2006)

5 In the diagram, *T* is a point on a circle, centre *O*.
PT is the tangent to the circle at *T* so that angle *OTP* = 90°.
DOCP is a straight line so that *CD* is a diameter of the circle.

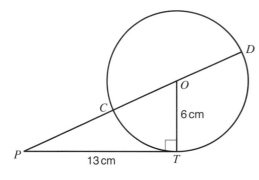

a Work out the length of *OP*.
Give your answer in cm correct to 1 decimal place.

b Hence work out the length of
i *PC* **ii** *PD*.
Give your answers in cm correct to 1 decimal place.

6 *PQRS* is a trapezium with the sides *PS* and *QR* parallel. *PQ* is perpendicular to both *PS* and *QR*.
QR = 8 cm, *RS* = 10 cm, *PS* = 12 cm.

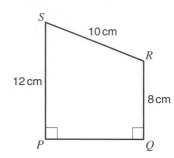

a Work out the length of *PQ*.
Give your answer in cm correct to 2 decimal places.

b Work out the area of trapezium *PQRS*.
Give your answer to the nearest cm².

7 The diagram shows a circle, a chord and two radii. The radius of the circle is 6.8 cm and the perpendicular distance of the chord from the centre of the circle is 5.2 cm.

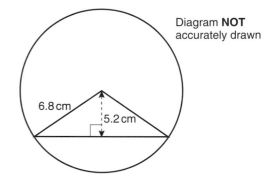

Diagram **NOT** accurately drawn

Work out the length of the chord.
Give your answer in cm correct to 2 decimal places.

(1385 June 2001)